# ATOMS AND THE UNIVERSE

# ATOMS AND THE UNIVERSE

An account of modern views on the structure
of matter and the universe

*by*

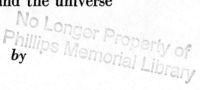

## G. O. JONES

*Professor of Physics in the University of
London at Queen Mary College*

## J. ROTBLAT

*Professor of Physics in the University of
London at St. Bartholomew's Hospital
Medical College*

## G. J. WHITROW

*Reader in Applied Mathematics in the
University of London at the Imperial College
of Science and Technology*

*with a prefatory note by*
SIR JOHN COCKCROFT, K.C.B.

## CHARLES SCRIBNER'S SONS
### New York

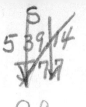

Copyright© 1956
by G. O. Jones, J. Rotblat and G. J. Whitrow
This book is copyright under the Berne Convention

PRINTED IN THE UNITED STATES OF AMERICA

# Contents

# Figures

# *Figures*

# *Tables*

# Plates

9

# *Prefatory Note*

A*toms and the Universe* will appeal both to students of science and to the general reader interested in scientific development, by its presentation in simple language of the basic experimental work and concepts of nuclear physics and the relations of nuclear physics to the larger and fascinating problems of the universe and its development.

J. D. COCKCROFT.

# *Preface*

The aim of this book is to provide the general reader with a survey of modern physics extending from the smallest known objects to the largest. To do this in a few hundred pages we must abandon one of the main characteristics of scientific method – its insistence upon rigour in argument and explanation – and simplify the discussion as far as possible without sacrificing essential truth. Fortunately, our readers will probably be familiar with the general sense of words like *force, momentum, energy, wavelength*, which constantly appear in the following pages. Only when it is absolutely necessary to make meanings more precise or to introduce unfamiliar terms have we insisted on more rigorous definition.

Our general scheme is almost the reverse of historical, for we begin with the smallest objects, atoms and their constituent particles, which have been studied by men of science only within the present century. We then proceed to explain how atoms cohere to produce the many forms of matter, and to discuss its behaviour. This is the world of familiar phenomena which was the main study of scientists during the 19th century. Finally, we move out of the laboratory to consider the largest objects – the planets and stars. This is where physical science began. So, starting with atoms we end by discussing the universe. In attending to details at all these levels there is a risk of failing to see the wood for the trees. We have tried to avoid this by including some account of the important unifying principles in science.

The detailed arrangement is as follows: We begin with an introduction concerning the methods of science, showing that it is a continuous body of knowledge and not merely a collection of unrelated subjects. The first chapters contain descriptions of the fundamental particles of matter, such as protons, neutrons and electrons, and of the phenomena associated with them, such as radioactivity, nuclear disintegration, fission and fusion. The problem of tapping nuclear energy and some of the fascinating questions associated with the cosmic ray particles are also discussed.

Unlike these topics, which have been studied only within the last fifty years, the investigation of the structure and properties of matter in bulk, which forms our next subject, has always been a part of science. However, it has advanced beyond recognition during the present century owing to the tremendous progress made in physics and chemistry. At this stage we take the opportunity of discussing the impact upon scientific thought of the two main theoretical developments of the period, relativity and quantum theory, which have a bearing on the topics of every chapter in the book.

Finally, we come to the discoveries of astronomers and astrophysicists concerning the nature and structure of our sun and galaxy. In this field too the last half-century has seen a revolutionary advance in knowledge, much of which would have been impossible without the major discoveries described in earlier chapters. We conclude with a general survey of current ideas about the size and age of the universe with their puzzling but fascinating implications. Some general remarks about the background of scientific research and the role of mathematics and theory in physics are given in an Appendix.

The text is based on a series of lectures organized by the Extramural Department of the University of London and the Croydon Education Committee. The reception given to these lectures showed that men and women with no scientific experience or training were anxious to understand and discuss many of the most difficult questions in modern physics and astrophysics when these were explained to them in clear and simple terms.

This open-minded attitude towards scientific advance is one of the most encouraging signs in the world today. The intelligent layman who is not content merely to be the puppet of fortune wants to understand why science, which at one time seemed to be interesting but remote, now plays so large and exciting a part in human affairs. He is anxious to know why its misuse is so full of danger, while its proper application holds out so grand a prospect for the future of mankind. In this book we have tried to help him to understand how this situation has come about.

G.O.J.
J.R.
*September* 1955.                                                    G.J.W.

# ATOMS AND THE UNIVERSE

# Introduction

*The study of the physical world*

By the simple act of looking around him and seeing material objects, inquiring man at once confronts the main problems faced by the scientist. For he is not satisfied for long merely to look at material objects; he very soon wants to know of what they are made and how they behave. That is, he wishes to understand the structure, constitution and properties of matter. Next, he may ask how it is that he sees objects. He is now asking what are the properties of light, how it is emitted or reflected from matter, and how it affects the retina of his eye. So far he has asked questions which a physicist would try to answer. He will probably continue by asking how it is that he, a particular kind of lump of matter, has the ability to translate the images on the retina into mental images, and indeed, to ask such questions. Ultimately he may ask how (or perhaps *why*) it is that he exists at all. He has already ventured into biology, metaphysics and philosophy.

In this book, while we aim to survey the physical world as a whole, it will be found that most of the discussion is about the facts and problems of physics. Do we imply that physics covers the whole physical world? This is an important question, which it is worth pausing to examine, because this will give us at once a view of the content of science and of the inter-relations between its branches.

Let us admit at once that the world is not all physics, in any conventional sense. Nor, indeed, would it be claimed that all the other well-known branches of science are in any way subordinate to physics. However, the borders between physics and astronomy, chemistry, biology, or geology – to name a few of the most important sciences – are less real than most people imagine, and physics has a rather special and fundamental role to play in relation to these other sciences. Let us consider first physics, astronomy and chemistry. It will be necessary to say something about forces, and about the motions to which they give rise, in order to have a basis for discussion.

Force is one of the commonest themes in physics. It is found in nature that bodies can act upon each other with various kinds of force which are distinguishable from each other. For example, there is the gravitational force of attraction, which exists between all massive bodies. This is the force which keeps the moon and planets in their orbits, and causes bodies on the earth to fall, although it is not easy to detect the gravitational force between small bodies except by very careful experiments. There are also electric forces between electric charges which can be easily demonstrated by rubbing the case of a fountain pen on one's sleeve. This causes loose electricity to appear on the case, which will then attract light objects such as small pieces of paper. Then there are magnetic forces of attraction or repulsion such as exist between magnets, or between magnets and pieces of iron, which are easily detected by the simplest methods.

Physics deals in detail with the nature of all these forces, and with their effects. A familiar example is the case of a body falling to the earth under the action of the downward gravitational force of attraction between it and the earth; in the absence of air the speed of fall would become greater and greater indefinitely. Actually it becomes constant when the upward force of drag due to the air becomes as great as the downward gravitational force – when there is no net force acting on the body. The 'physical laws' which govern such motions are constantly demonstrated and verified in elementary physics laboratories, but the important truth for us is that exactly the same laws govern the motions of the stars and planets. Thus physics and astronomy are part of a continuum; while astronomy deals with the motions of heavenly bodies, these motions are governed by physical laws which form one part of the province of physics. We would say that the part of this continuum of knowledge which is essentially physics concerns the fundamental nature of the laws relating to forces and motions; the part which is essentially astronomy concerns the detailed motions of the stars and planets.

As physics and astronomy have developed, the continuity between them has been demonstrated in many other ways. Thus, while the study of the nature of light is one of the main branches of physics, it has become clear that the study of the light emitted by stars is one of the most powerful methods by which their natures can be found – and is, therefore, of great importance in astronomy. Several other examples of the continuity between physics and astronomy will be mentioned in this book.

## Physics and chemistry

Let us consider next the relation between physics and chemistry. Now chemistry is, essentially, the study of the differences between substances. To make use of an example: everyone knows that the substance water is represented by '$H_2O$' even though the significance of this symbol may not be understood. What it means is that the smallest 'unit' of water which can exist (a molecule of water) consists of two atoms of hydrogen, represented by '$H_2$', and one atom of oxygen, represented by 'O', stuck together in some way. These atoms can be separated, for instance, by passing an electric current through water, so that we again have pure hydrogen gas and oxygen gas. This process is called the electrolysis of water. Conversely, the oxygen and hydrogen can be re-formed into water by an electric spark. A very large body of knowledge has been built up over many centuries concerning the ways in which different substances can be formed and transformed. It has been found that there exist in nature about ninety different kinds of atom which can behave as fundamental units. Hydrogen and oxygen atoms are two examples, hydrogen and oxygen accordingly being known as elements. Another example is uranium, the heaviest of the naturally existing elements. When atoms of two or more elements stick together (or 'combine') they can form molecules of other substances known as compounds, of which water is an example.

With ninety kinds of brick one might expect to be able to build very many different kinds of structure and it is true that the number of chemical compounds which can exist is without limit. The lightest element, hydrogen, can combine with nearly every other element, and indeed, nearly every element can combine with nearly every other. Chemistry is thus a limitless subject in its own right. It is indeed extraordinary how far chemistry developed before the real properties of individual atoms had been discovered. Their existence was tacitly assumed by chemists as necessary for the development of any logical pattern in their subject.

Now just as physics deals with the fundamental laws governing the motions of the stars and planets, it attempts to deal also with the fundamental aspects of the discoveries of chemistry, that is, to explain why some elements combine with others under certain circumstances or can be separated under other circumstances. It attempts to discover what is the 'glue' which sticks atoms together to form molecules. In this respect it has in the present century been brilliantly successful. The discoveries made in physics about the nature of atoms have also shown why atoms should stick together. In spite of the enormous complexity of this problem the reasons are known, at least in principle. One of the important types of force is simply electrical. In water, for example, the atoms stick together largely because they become electrically charged. By the application of an electric force, in electrolysis, they can be drawn apart. At this point, where we have a typical physical process leading to typical chemical results, physics and chemistry are inseparable and indistinguishable.

It is common for physicists when speaking to chemists to say that chemistry is a branch of physics – a remark which is meant to draw attention to the fact that physicists study those aspects of the facts of chemistry which appear to be the more fundamental, leaving it to chemists to work out the details of particular cases. The chemist might retort that physics is a tool, which he uses to solve his own problems, and the impartial reader will perhaps be content to draw the conclusion that, at least, the two subjects must be part of a continuous whole.

*Physics and biology*

So far, we have mentioned phenomena which differ in scale rather than in kind. But where do the biological sciences stand? Is there not something different about sciences which deal with the study of life? The answer, in so far as these questions can be answered, may be somewhat surprising to the reader, and it contains a notable demonstration of the rather dispassionate attitude which natural science adopts even to such questions as

"What is life?" which are so significant in philosophy and metaphysics.

The development of biology has been a gradual change from mere classification, through the emergence of general principles such as those of the evolutionary theory, to a synthesis with physics and chemistry which is quite as important for its ultimate development as was the synthesis with physics for the development of chemistry. The mechanisms of such biological processes as cell-division, when studied purely as physical and chemical processes, are found to be purely physical and chemical processes. Of course, the living processes are not those normally studied by physicists and chemists, but they are not fundamentally different in kind and it would be quite possible to list a sequence of different processes, running from the ordinary chemical to the ordinary biological, in which each step was too small to represent a real difference in kind. At no point in the sequence could we agree that we had passed in a single step from a non-living to a living activity. Of course, in a very large number of such steps, the difference between a man and a lump of metal could be encompassed and we do not assert that a man is the same kind of thing as a lump of metal. But in trying to answer the question "What is life?" we are somewhat at a loss since it would hardly be a sufficient answer to point to the two ends of our sequence and to say that life, or the absence of life, was what distinguished them from each other. In this dilemma, which is the model dilemma of philosophy, it is useful to remember Humpty-Dumpty's assertion in *Alice through the Looking-glass*: "When I use a word, it means what I choose it to mean, neither more nor less." The facts about life appear to be in essence as stated above – although of course they have been grossly over-simplified, and too hastily stated. What we choose to regard as the boundary between living and non-living is purely a matter of convention.

Some of the latest developments in biology have resulted from the application of the newest ideas and techniques of physics and chemistry. It is not always possible to distinguish between ideas and techniques, but we should draw attention to the fact that physics, for instance, has links with biology which depend on the application of physical techniques. The most important demonstration of this probably lies in the use of the microscope. Its invention was made possible by the discovery of the laws governing the reflection of light and the behaviour of light in passing through materials such as glass – matters which were the typical concern of early physicists. More recently, we have seen the introduction of instruments such as the electron microscope, which depend on some of the later discoveries of physics, as well as of many new methods of analysis developed by chemists, all used to provide new and powerful tools for the biologist.

Finally, we might remind the reader that a glance at the shelves of a scientific bookseller, or at the prospectus of a large university, will amply demonstrate the truth of the present argument. For there he will find that there exist text-books, and professors, not only of physics, chemistry, mathematics and biology, but also of mathematical physics, chemical physics, astrophysics, biophysics, geophysics, physical chemistry, biochemistry, biomathematics, as well as of many other strange combinations. However, in this book we shall, as already suggested, be concerned most immediately with that part of nature which is rather close to the centre of the domain of physics; in particular, the domain of biology will receive much less attention than its due.

## The methods of experimental science

We now illustrate, by choosing as examples a few famous experiments, some of the leading features of experimental science upon which, in the last resort, all the content of science depends. Experiments can be of many kinds. The well-known experiment of Galileo, who rolled balls of different weights down an inclined plane, gives an example of one of the characteristic methods of approach of experimental science in that it had a definite object, and yielded a definite result. On other occasions the discoveries of science seem to be almost accidental, although even then the scientist is usually looking for something. It is usually no accident that he is looking where he is, even if he does not know for what he is looking. The discovery of penicillin by Fleming is a well-known example of an apparently accidental discovery, because this depended on the lucky event that a spore of a common green mould settled on a culture plate upon which bacteria were under examination. Of course, it required a man of Fleming's acumen to realize the significance of the event. Equally, it required the most refined chemical techniques, and the skill and perseverance of Florey, Chain and their colleagues before the active substance could be extracted in the laboratory, many years later.

One of the most famous experiments of all time was the identification of the electron by J. J. Thomson in 1897. This is a very appropriate experiment to select for more detailed discussion because it will introduce many concepts which will later be useful to the reader. Thomson's experiment is usually regarded as marking a turning-point in physics, since the electron, one of the fundamental particles of which atoms are made up, was the first such particle to be discovered. Today, electrons are put busily to use in all the modern devices of electronics, such as radio and television receivers, electronic computers, and devices for the automatic control of industrial processes and the automatic guiding of missiles.

It had been discovered earlier that when an electric current was passed through a gas (in the 'discharge tube') under certain conditions, a beam of some kind travelled in the tube from the negative to the positive terminal, that is, in the direction opposite to that which had conventionally been accepted as the direction of flow of current. This beam of cathode rays could be made to cause scintillations on a suitable screen; an object placed in the way would then cast a shadow on the screen, indicating that the beam normally travelled in a straight line. A barrier pierced with a small hole could be used to select a narrow 'pencil' out of the main beam in order to show its path more clearly (Fig. 1). It was already known as a result of the discoveries of the 18th and 19th centuries that electric charges could be caused to move by the application of electric forces and also that a wire carrying a current could be caused to move by the application of a magnetic force, say by a magnet. In this case the direction of motion is at right angles both to the direction of the current and to that of the magnetic force. The physical laws governing these motions had indeed become an accepted part of physics. Now when electric or magnetic forces were applied at right angles *across* the path of the beam it was found that the beam was deflected

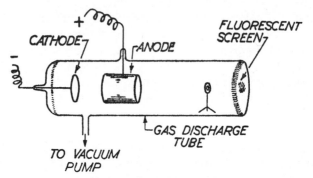

FIG. 1. *Cathode ray tube.*

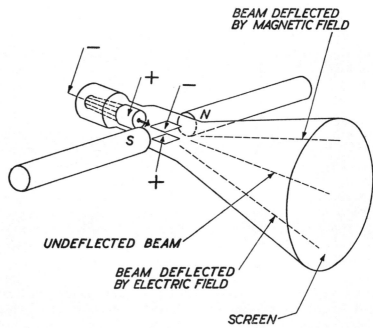

FIG. 2. *J. J. Thomson's identification of the electron.*

*as a whole.* These results were sufficient in themselves to show that the beam consisted of a stream of negatively charged identical particles whose flow constituted at least part of the current.

The experiment of J. J. Thomson, which is illustrated in Fig. 2, was to make use of these deflections in order to establish for the individual particles the value of the quantity $e/m$ – the ratio of the electric charge $e$ to the mass $m$. The method consisted of applying a transverse electric force in order to deflect the beam and then finding what magnetic force applied in the other transverse direction would just return the beam to its original path. Knowing the magnitudes of the electric and magnetic forces applied he could obtain the value of $e/m$. We need not worry here about the mathematical analysis required in devising the experiment and in working out the result (see Appendix). But it is worth reminding ourselves that all that was actually observed about these particles was the point of impact of the beam, and the experiment had to be designed to make this a useful observation.

The significance of the result was enormous. By showing that a definite value for $e/m$ existed Thomson had really discovered the electron – as this new particle was called – even though its manifestations had already been seen in the observations which had led up to his experiment. It is usual to speak of this experiment as the identification of the electron, and this is perhaps just. Also, since the same value was obtained whatever gas was contained in the tube, the particle identified was clearly a sub-atomic particle – that is, a constituent particle of atoms. From that time on, any other sub-atomic or new particle could be subjected to some similar test in order to see whether it was of the same kind.

The necessity for exact measurement of the kind exemplified in this experiment is very characteristic of physics, and it is of interest to consider what would be involved in this case in making the experiment an accurate one. The final answer depends on knowing the magnitudes of certain applied electric forces and magnetic forces. In practice we must always set up some convenient unit or standard before any physical quantity can be measured – that is, before its magnitude can be given a number, and the reader will be aware of the existence, for example, of volts and centimetres. A convenient unit of electric force is the volt per centimetre. If a 1-volt battery were connected across parallel plates 1 centimetre apart, the electric force between the plates would be 1 volt per centimetre. So in the Thomson experiment it would first be necessary to make sure that the parallel plates really were quite parallel, and to measure the distance apart very accurately. Then it would be necessary to determine the voltage across the plates, let us say, with a voltmeter. The reader will be familiar with instruments which do not necessarily read correctly – perhaps he has suffered from errors in the indication given by a petrol gauge on a motor car. In physics the question of accuracy in instruments is vital. The voltmeter would have to be very well constructed in order to make sure that a given voltage always caused the same deflection of the pointer. At the time of manufacture it would be compared with a standard instrument of known accuracy. And, of course, most important, the standard instrument itself would have been made in such a way that it read '1 volt' when subjected to the voltage defined as 1 volt. That is, the definition of the unit known as the volt must in itself imply a method by which its measurement can be realized in practice. We have considered rather hastily some of the experimental problems which would be involved in measuring the electric force in an experiment of the Thomson type; these are rather more easily explained than those associated with the magnetic force, but of course both have to be measured, and in a complex modern experiment very many more quantities might have to be measured accurately at the same time.

The next step in the history of the electron was that scientists tried to devise means of measuring its mass, or its charge, separately. The first accurate experiment of this kind was performed by R. A. Millikan in 1909. He found that minute oil droplets floating in a chamber and observed by a microscope could be made to pick up charges and could then be held suspended, or accelerated upward or downward, by an electric force applied across parallel plates. The charge, determined by measuring the rate of motion under a given electric force, always varied by multiples of a certain unit of charge. He presumed, as we now know correctly, that this 'highest common factor' was the charge of a single electron, and *e* was thus determined. By making use of this result in conjunction with Thomson's value of $e/m$ it was then a simple matter to work out the value of *m*, the electronic mass. This turned out to be very much smaller than the masses of atoms; it is about $\frac{1}{1800}$ of the mass of the hydrogen atom.

In Millikan's experiment, perhaps more than in Thomson's, experimental skill and refinement of the highest order were necessary. For Thomson measured only the *ratio* between two quantities which were minutely small by comparison with the electric charges and masses normally studied in the laboratory. But Millikan actually observed the effects of single electrons, each equivalent to an electric charge of only $4\cdot8 \times 10^{-10}$ or 4·8/10,000,000,000 electrostatic units of charge. The significance of this can be seen when one realizes that the choice of the unit of charge is made arbitrarily in order to have a size convenient for ordinary experiments in the laboratory. (An electrostatic unit of charge is one which will exert a force upon a similar charge at a distance of 1 centimetre equal to that which has been chosen to be the unit of force.) So Millikan observed the effects of charges which were smaller by a factor of about $10^{10}$ (or 10,000,000,000) than those which would normally have been examined in laboratory experiments on electricity – a feat of refined experimenting which has since been emulated in many of the experiments of physics.

Physics has travelled a long way since the experiments of Thomson and Millikan. It is interesting, however, to take another look at Fig. 2, for this is almost exactly the form of the modern television tube. In these tubes, electrons strike a fluorescent screen at points determined by the signal transmitted from the transmitting station. Indeed, the Thomson tube is also the forerunner of one of the most powerful tools of experimental science, the electron microscope. We have already seen how a beam of electrons can be made to travel in a straight line and can also be deflected, or bent, just as a beam of light is bent in a lens or prism. The special significance of using electrons for microscopy is that they are very small, and can be made to 'see' things which are too small to be seen by the use of light. For, just as the long radio waves can go around corners, the much shorter light waves fail to identify objects much shorter than their wavelength. The wavelength of ordinary visible light is still quite large by atomic standards – perhaps 1,000–5,000 times the diameter of an atom, so that objects consisting of, say, hundreds or millions of atoms, which in linear dimension would be only tens or hundreds of atomic sizes, would still be too small to be seen in any optical microscope. In biology, in particular, many of the most important objects have sizes in this region and in Plate II we see one of the first photographs ever taken by the electron microscope of quite fine detail in a chromosome, known by biologists to carry the genes which are mainly responsible for the transmission of hereditary characteristics. In the plate a photograph taken by ultra-violet light (the shortest light waves which can be used in conventional microscopy) is also shown for comparison. We see again how close the various branches of science can come to each other.

In the pages which follow, the reader will be presented with experimental, observational and theoretical results derived from a multitude of researches. In general, there will be no opportunity to explain how these results were obtained, but we hope that this short introduction will have helped to make the reader aware of the typical background behind the main conclusions of scientific research. Some further discussion of this background will be found in the Appendix.

# CHAPTER I

# *Elementary particles*

### *The atomists and the alchemists*

What is the structure of matter? Is there anything in common in the make-up of different substances, in a rose and a ruby; in a piece of brass and the human brain? If there is, what is the nature of the prime materials, of the simple bricks of which all matter is built? How many are there? Are they really the simplest forms of matter, or can they be still further divided? This sort of question engaged the mind and aroused the curiosity of man ever since he learned to think. Throughout the history of civilization one can discern a strong desire to solve the riddle of the structure of matter, to shed light on the nature of the elementary particles of which it is supposed to be composed. It was not until the 20th century that real progress was made towards finding an answer to these questions, and even now we have no complete solution to the problem.

The early concepts of the structure of matter appear to have their origin in ancient Greek philosophy. In the 5th century B.C. the atomistic hypothesis was put forward by Leucippus and Democritus. According to them, all substances are built up of small units called atoms which are the smallest fragments into which a given substance can be divided. This is implied in the name 'atom' which means 'indivisible'. At about the same time a different hypothesis was put forward by Empedocles and later developed by Aristotle. They believed that all matter consists of one primordial substance, called hyle, or ylem, which is identical in all bodies. The difference between various substances is due to the presence in them in varying quantities of certain qualities imposed on the prime matter by the four elements, fire, earth, air and water.

The great authority of Aristotle was probably responsible for the general acceptance of this concept for over two thousand years. It formed the basis of alchemy, which in the Middle Ages was the forerunner of modern nuclear physics. The alchemists' aim was to transform elements, particularly to make noble metals from base ones. In order to achieve this they tried to obtain pure prime matter by taking away from a substance its four elements. They thought that once having achieved this the transmutation of elements could be easily accomplished by adding the four elements in the suitable proportions.

The complete failure of the alchemist brought to the foreground the long neglected atomistic concept, which became an established theory by the beginning of the 19th century, mainly due to the work of John Dalton. From consideration of the ways in which various elements combine together to form chemical compounds, Dalton arrived at the conclusion that every element is built up of atoms which are the indestructible and indivisible units of matter. The atoms of each chemical element are identical but different from atoms of other elements. Since we now know of about a hundred different chemical elements, including those produced artificially, it would follow from Dalton's theory that there are that number of elementary particles. This is not a very satisfactory conclusion. It is somewhat difficult to accept the idea that so many different types of brick have to be used in the structure of the universe. How much simpler and more attractive seemed the hypothesis, put forward by W. Prout in 1816, that the atoms of all elements are built up of one atom, the atom of hydrogen, which would thus correspond to the prime matter, the ylem of the Greeks. Prout based his idea on the assumption that the atomic weights of all elements were whole numbers and, therefore, multiples of the atomic weight of hydrogen, which is given unit value. This assumption proved to be incorrect when, stimulated by Prout's hypothesis, more accurate measurements of atomic weights were carried out and found in many cases to have fractional values, as for example 35·457 for chlorine, or 63·54 for copper. Prout's hypothesis was thus abandoned, but only temporarily, for it was revived in a modified form a century later.

The fact chiefly responsible for this revival was the discovery of radioactivity and the evidence it has brought that the atom is destructible. But even before this discovery a number of phenomena became known which had a decisive influence on our ideas of the structure of matter. These phenomena, which deal with the discharge of electricity in gases at low pressures, could only be observed following the development of vacuum techniques, *i.e.* of methods of producing low pressures. These, in turn, came about as a result of the remarkable progress made in the kinetic theory of gases in the latter half of the 19th century.

### The electron

The passage of electricity through gases at low pressures was the subject of study by a number of scientists, notably by E. Goldstein in Germany and W. Crookes in Great Britain. If an electric potential difference of several thousand volts is applied to two terminals inserted at the ends of a glass tube, from which the air can be pumped out, it is found that at a sufficiently low pressure a green glow, or luminescence, appears in the tube. The cause of this luminescence can be traced to some radiation originating at the negative terminal, the cathode; for this reason the radiation was given the name 'cathode rays'.

The nature and properties of the cathode rays were fully investigated by J. J. Thomson as already described in the Introduction. In these experiments the existence of a particle much lighter than the lightest of all atoms was established for the first time. This particle was given the name 'electron', and we know now that its mass is 1,837 times smaller than that of the hydrogen atom, and that the electric charge it carries is the smallest that can occur; in fact, every electric charge is an integral multiple of the charge of the electron.

An important fact revealed in these studies was that, although the velocity of the cathode rays was variable, depending on the voltage applied to the tube, the charge and the mass of the electrons was always the same. It remained constant and independent of the nature of the gas in the tube or of the material of the electrodes.

Cathode rays are not the only means of producing electrons. In fact, three other phenomena in which electrons are emitted

B

were discovered at about the same time. One was the so-called
'photo-electric effect', which has nowadays many practical uses,
notably in television. It occurs when substances, particularly the
alkali metals, are irradiated with visible light, or still better with
ultra-violet light. A stream of particles is then found to issue
from the metal, and these particles were identified as electrons.
Another effect is the so-called 'thermionic emission', which is the
basis of the functioning of all radio valves. If a metal filament is
heated to a high temperature, charged particles are emitted from
it which can produce fluorescence on a screen, as in a television
tube, or cause an electric current to flow in a circuit. These
particles too were identified as electrons. Finally, it was found
that electrons were emitted spontaneously from certain elements,
the radioactive substances. These are very fast electrons, and
before they were identified as such were given the name of
$\beta$-rays.

The amazing fact is that although produced in such a variety
of ways, all these rays have the same properties, the same electric
charge, and the same mass if a correction is made for the variation of mass with velocity which follows from the relativity
theory (see Chapter VII). No matter whether they are produced
in solids or in gases, at low or high temperatures, at atmospheric
pressure or in vacuum, by irradiation with light or by spontaneous
emission, they are all identical. The obvious conclusion is that the
electrons go into the make-up of all elements and that, therefore,
they are a universal constituent of matter. It has proved impossible to produce a charge smaller than that carried by an
electron, or to break it up into smaller fragments. The electron
may thus be considered to be an elementary particle.

### The proton

Although electrons have proved to be ingredients of all elements
they cannot be the only constituents of matter. For one thing,
electrons are negatively charged, while atoms are normally neutral; there must, therefore, exist particles of positive charge.
Moreover, the mass of the electron is far too small to account for
the mass of the atom. The clue to the identity of the other

elementary particles came as a result of the discovery of radio-activity.

The subject of radioactivity will be discussed in detail in the next chapter, but a general outline will be useful here. Thanks to the work of Becquerel in 1895, and of Marie and Pierre Curie in the following years, it was established that the heaviest elements existing in nature, such as uranium, thorium, radium and polonium, have the property of sending out radiations spontaneously. These radiations are known as α-, β- and γ-rays. As has already been stated, β-rays are fast-moving electrons; α-rays were found to be positively charged heavier particles, and γ-rays were shown to be electromagnetic waves. The most revolutionary discovery made in radioactivity was that after the emission of these radiations the atoms of a given radioactive substance are transformed into atoms of a different chemical element; in most cases these are also radioactive and in turn undergo a further transformation. By 1902 Rutherford and Soddy had established the laws governing the transformation of radioactive elements and had shown how the various radioactive substances can be arranged in three families, which start with uranium and thorium and end with lead after a whole series of transformations. Here, for the first time, the dream of the alchemist, the transmutation of elements, came true. It was found to be a spontaneous process which had been going on undetected for ages. Obviously, if an atom can break up and change into another, then it cannot be considered an elementary particle. The discovery of radioactivity thus brought to an end the belief that atoms are indivisible and elementary particles of matter.

Further experiments with radioactive substances, mainly the investigations on the scattering of α-particles made by Rutherford, gave an intimation of the structure of the atom. From these experiments, and the theory put forward by Niels Bohr in 1913, the nuclear model of the atom was evolved. According to this, each atom resembles a solar system; it is built up of a central core, or nucleus, and of a number of electrons revolving around it at various distances. The nucleus is positively charged, and the number of electrons is such that their charge exactly balances the positive charge of the nucleus so that the atom as a whole is

Fig. 3. The periodic table of elements.

electrically neutral. The number of electrons revolving round the nucleus in an atom has proved to be a very important property of the atom. It defines the numerical place occupied by the given element in the Periodic Table of Elements (Fig. 3); for this reason it is called the 'atomic number'. Thus, hydrogen, which has one electron in its atom, occupies the first place in the Table; helium with two electrons, the second place; oxygen the eighth; uranium the ninety-second. The atomic number also determines the chemical properties of the given element, since all chemical processes are caused by changes in the configuration of the electrons; the nucleus itself does not take any part in these processes. Rutherford's scattering experiments also revealed that the nucleus is extremely small, its radius is about ten thousand times smaller than that of the atom, but despite its minuteness it contains practically all the mass of the atom. The nucleus is, therefore, the seat of matter, and in order to find out about the structure of matter it is necessary to tackle the problem of the structure of the nucleus.

The first clear concepts of the constitution of the nucleus emerged in 1919. By that time it had been established, mainly due to the work of F. W. Aston, that most elements are not simple, but consist of a mixture of several types of atoms differing from each other in weight. The various types of atoms of a given element are called isotopes; all isotopes of one element have the same atomic number, i.e. the same number of electrons in their atoms, and consequently they have all the same chemical properties, but their nuclei have different weights. The analysis of the isotopic composition of an element can be carried out by means of a method analogous to that used by J. J. Thomson to determine the properties of the electron. An instrument called the mass spectrometer is used, which employs a combination of electric and magnetic fields. The atoms of the given element are ionized by knocking out electrons from them and thus making them positively charged. In the electric and magnetic fields ions of different masses are deflected by different amounts. By observing into how many groups a given beam of ions splits, the number of isotopes can be determined; by measuring the deflection of each group the atomic weight of the individual isotopes can be calculated.

The determination of the atomic weights of individual isotopes revealed the amazing fact that they were all very nearly integral numbers, that is to say, that they could be expressed as almost exact multiples of the atomic weight of hydrogen. Thus, for example, chlorine, which has an atomic weight of 35·457, was found to be a mixture of two isotopes, one of which has an atomic weight of 34·978 and the other 36·977; similarly copper was found to have two isotopes of atomic weights nearly 63 and 65. This discovery brought back to life the old hypothesis of Prout in a slightly modified form; it has now become possible to assume that the nuclei of all elements are built up of the nucleus of the hydrogen atom. This nucleus, which carries one elementary positive charge, was given the name 'proton'.

Although this assumption was very attractive, it would have been little more than a hypothesis without direct proof that protons are indeed present in nuclei of other elements. This proof was given by Rutherford in an epoch-making experiment in 1919, in which he effected the disintegration of the nitrogen nucleus, the first man-made transmutation of elements. Rutherford bombarded nitrogen atoms with α-particles from radioactive substances and demonstrated that protons were emitted as a result of the disintegration. Later, similar experiments were carried out with other elements and in these cases too the emission of protons was established beyond doubt. Thus, definite evidence was obtained that protons enter into the structure of nuclei of other elements and that, therefore, the proton is an elementary particle of matter.

*The neutron*

The disintegration experiments provided definite proof that protons are components of nuclei of all elements, but protons by themselves are not sufficient to make up a nucleus. This can be seen clearly when one considers the relationship between atomic number and atomic weight of any element. Oxygen, for example, occupies the eighth place in the Periodic Table. This means that the atom of oxygen contains 8 electrons revolving round its nucleus, and consequently the nucleus of oxygen must contain 8 positive charges, *i.e.* 8 protons. On the other hand, the atomic weight of oxygen is 16, which means that the nucleus is 16 times heavier than the hydrogen atom, and so would require the presence of 16 protons. How can we account for this discrepancy? The simplest way is to assume that in addition to the orbital electrons there are some electrons in the nucleus. Thus, the nucleus of oxygen might consist of 16 protons and 8 electrons. The 8 electrons would neutralize 8 positive charges of the protons, making an effective charge of 8, while the total mass would still be 16 since the electrons hardly contribute to the weight. In a similar way, the charge and mass of all other nuclei could be explained by assuming that apart from protons they contain a certain number of electrons. The existence of electrons in the nucleus is seemingly also supported by the fact that some of the radioactive elements emit electrons when they break up. It might be argued that if an electron can be emitted from a nucleus, it must have been there before.

In this way the whole problem of the structure of matter became greatly simplified. All matter could be assumed to be built up of only two particles, protons and electrons. This solution, though attractive in its simplicity, as it brought down the number of components of matter to a minimum, could not, however, be upheld, and a number of flaws were soon found in it. The main objection was the assumed presence of electrons in the nucleus. As the development of nuclear physics proceeded, more and more experimental and theoretical evidence accumulated, which was at variance with this simple scheme, and which particularly contradicted the idea that electrons were present in the nucleus. One of these difficulties can be explained by means of the following example of the nucleus of nitrogen. Nitrogen has atomic number 7 and atomic weight 14. We would, therefore, have to assume that its nucleus contains 14 protons and 7 electrons, altogether 21 particles. On the other hand, from the molecular spectrum of nitrogen, as well as from other evidence, it appears that the nucleus of nitrogen must contain an even number of particles.

Perhaps the strongest argument against the existence of electrons in the nucleus is of a theoretical nature. One can calculate the magnitude of the force needed to confine the negatively charged electron within the boundary of the positively charged nucleus, and this force turned out to be several hundred times greater than that actually observed in the nucleus. All these considerations add up to the simple statement that there is no place for electrons in the nucleus. But, if so, what is there to take the place of these electrons?

The answer to this question came in 1932, when Chadwick discovered the neutron. The neutron is a particle of approximately the same mass as the proton, but without an electric charge. Its discovery was the result of experiments carried out by physicists in several countries. First, W. Bothe and H. Becker in Germany observed that when some light elements are bombarded with α-particles, they send out a very penetrating radiation which they thought to be γ-rays of a high energy. Next, Irene Curie and Frederick Joliot in France found that if these rays are made to collide with hydrogen atoms, fast protons are emitted. The French scientists still upheld the γ-ray hypothesis and they thought that they had discovered a new mode of interaction of γ-rays with matter. Chadwick, however, immediately recognized the true nature of the penetrating rays and produced experimental evidence that they were particles and not waves. He deduced that the mass of these particles was about the same as that of the proton and gave the proper interpretation for their great penetrating power as due to the absence of electric charge, which means that they do not interact with electrons of the atoms through which they pass. Very soon afterwards it was found that a similar emission of neutrons is observed when other elements are bombarded with α-particles, and this provided proof that the neutron is a constituent of the nucleus.

Immediately after the discovery of the neutron it was recognized that it was no longer necessary to assume the presence of electrons in the nucleus. Thus, for example, in order to explain the charge and mass of the nucleus of oxygen, one need only assume that it contains 8 protons and 8 neutrons. The total mass is, therefore, 16, while the charge is only 8. Similarly, nitrogen would contain 7 protons and 7 neutrons, a total of 14 particles, an even number. Thus, electrons were no longer required to be present in the nucleus and the structure of all atoms could be explained as consisting of protons and neutrons in the nuclei and of electrons outside them.

This is the view still held now. All atoms are assumed to be built up of three elementary particles: protons, neutrons and electrons. The protons and neutrons make up the nucleus of the atom. They are called nucleons, and the total number of nucleons is called the mass number of the isotope. This is so because in the conventional system of atomic weights the mass number is very nearly the same as the atomic weight. Different isotopes of the same element have the same number of protons in their atoms but different numbers of neutrons. The number of protons is equal to the number of electrons revolving round the nucleus and this number is the atomic number of the element. The constitution of every atom is, therefore, completely defined by two numbers, the atomic number and the mass number.

## The positron

Although the problem of the constitution of atoms had thus been satisfactorily solved, there still remained the question whether the proton, neutron and electron are the only elementary particles. Almost before the simple theory outlined above was established, facts became known which demanded the existence of a few more.

The conclusion that electrons do not exist in the nucleus has probably raised a question in the reader's mind. How do we explain the phenomenon of $\beta$-decay, the spontaneous emission of electrons from the nuclei of radioactive atoms? If electrons do not exist in the nucleus, how do they suddenly appear at the moment when they are to be emitted? The answer is that this is exactly what happens. Electrons are not normally in the nucleus but are created there at the moment when they are to be ejected. This is a process analogous to the emission of light from the atom, or of heat from a burning substance. The light or the flame were not there before but were produced at the required instant.

At first sight this analogy may not appear to be justified, because in the case of light or heat we deal with energy, while in the case of $\beta$-decay we deal with the creation of a particle, a fragment of matter. This objection is, however, removed when one takes into account the principle of the equivalence of matter and energy, as formulated by Einstein in his theory of relativity, which will be discussed in Chapter VII. In accordance with this, matter and energy are equivalent; matter can change into energy and *vice versa*. Since the electron has a very small mass, a relatively small amount of energy, which can be readily found in the nucleus, is sufficient to create it. Thus, the creation of an electron does not imply the production of matter from nothing, but only a transformation from energy.

The electron, however, apart from having a mass has also an electric charge and this too cannot be created from nothing. The law of conservation of electric charge imposes certain conditions for the creation of an electron from energy, namely, that there must at the same time be created a particle with the same positive charge, a positive electron, so that their combined charge will be zero.

The possible existence of a positive electron, or positron, was first foreshadowed in 1928, when Dirac formulated his theory of the electron, from which it followed that apart from the negative electron there must also exist its positive counterpart. But it was not until 1932 that the positron was discovered experimentally. C. D. Anderson, an American scientist, studied the cosmic radiation (see Chapter V) by means of a cloud chamber. In this instrument the path of a charged particle can be rendered visible by suddenly expanding a volume saturated with water vapour. Droplets of water are then deposited on the ions formed along the path of the particle, which thus produces a trail somewhat similar to that left by an aircraft. If the cloud chamber is placed in a magnetic field, the path of the particle is curved and from the direction of curvature the sign of the charge can be deduced; from the density of the tracks it is possible to discriminate between a proton and an electron. The photograph given in Plate III is of historic interest as it shows the first track identified as that of a positron. The cloud chamber contained a metal plate and it is seen that the curvature of the track is greater above the plate than below. Since the curvature is the greater the smaller the energy, and since the particle must have lost some energy in passing through the plate, this proves that the particle must have been moving upwards. From the observed curvature and from the known direction of the magnetic field Anderson deduced that the particle must have been positively charged.

Soon after this discovery was made it turned out that it is not necessary to look for positrons in cosmic radiation because they can be very easily produced by several methods available in the laboratory. One of these is the already mentioned process of materialization of energy, *i.e.* the creation of a negative and positive electron from energy. Such pair production, as it is called, can be brought about when $\gamma$ rays of sufficiently high energy pass through the field of an atom. Such a $\gamma$-ray may then disappear altogether and in its place may appear a pair of particles, an electron and a positron. Plate IV shows such a process of pair production occurring in a cloud chamber. A beam of $\gamma$-rays is passed through the chamber and at the point indicated by the arrow a $\gamma$-ray has struck an atom of the gas filling the chamber and produced a pair of charged particles. Both tracks are of the same density but they are curved in opposite directions which shows that they are of opposite charges. Another source of positrons is the spontaneous emission of positive electrons from some radio-active substances, a process similar to $\beta$-decay. Thus, there seems to be no doubt about the existence of the positive electron.

If the positron is an elementary particle the question may be raised as to why the positron does not occur in nature as frequently as the electron. The reason is that soon after a positron is created it disappears as a result of a collision with an electron. This process is the reverse of pair production, annihilation of matter as contrasted with materialization of energy. When two opposite electrons meet they combine together and are converted into energy, into two $\gamma$-rays, or much less frequently into three $\gamma$-rays. Since the universe contains so many negative electrons, it follows that very soon after a positron is born it meets an electron and is annihilated. The average life of the positron is very short, about $10^{-10}$ second, but despite its short existence its properties have been fully investigated and found to be the same as those of the electron, except for the sign of the charge.

*The neutrino*

We must now return to the problem of β-decay and explain how an electron, or positron, is produced in a nucleus at the instant when it is to be emitted. This touches on one of the most difficult subjects in nuclear physics, the problem of nuclear forces. The components of nuclei, protons and neutrons, act on each other with certain specific attractive forces, which are quite unlike the electrical or gravitational forces with which we are familiar from everyday life. First, these forces are of a very short range, they act only when the two particles are very close together inside the nucleus; if the particles are a little bit further apart the force is no longer there. Secondly, they are exchange forces, which means that the particles attract each other by virtue of a feature which they keep exchanging. This feature is their identity; for example, the proton can change into a neutron and the neutron into a proton. We can visualize this action as follows: a neutron may be considered to be a combination of a proton and an electron. When a neutron meets a proton it gives off the electron, turning itself into a proton; the electron is taken up by the proton, which becomes a neutron. In this way the two particles have exchanged identities and it is this continuous exchange which constitutes the attraction between them. Similarly, a proton may be considered to be a neutron plus a positron, and the latter is exchanged with another neutron. One may deduce from this that the proton and neutron can be considered as two different states of the same particle; in one state it is a proton and in the other a neutron. The exchange of neutrons and protons was confirmed experimentally from observations on collisions of fast neutrons with hydrogen.

The process of exchange described above goes on in the nucleus without producing any change in its constitution or emission of any radiation. There are, however, circumstances when a particle may change its identity without an exchange with another. This happens in the case of an unstable or radioactive nucleus. A radioactive nucleus is one which has the wrong constitution, it has either too many neutrons or too many protons. In the first case this can be remedied if one of the neutrons becomes a proton. The electron which has to be created at the same time to preserve the balance of charge cannot exist in the nucleus and is immediately emitted. We observe then the emission of $\beta$-rays. Similarly, if a nucleus has a surplus of protons, one of the protons may change into a neutron. A positive electron is then created and immediately emitted. This explains the emission of positive electrons from some radioactive elements.

It may be remarked here that the neutron itself is an unstable particle. If it is allowed to exist outside the nucleus for a long enough time, it breaks up spontaneously into a proton and an electron.

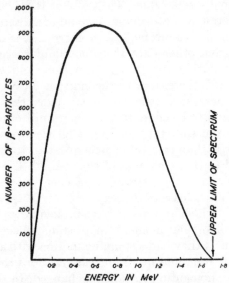

FIG. 4. *Energy spectrum of $\beta$-rays.*

The above scheme explains how electrons can be emitted from nuclei, but the process of $\beta$-decay presented yet other difficult problems. One of them concerns the energy of the emitted electrons. When radioactive atoms break up with the emission of $\beta$-rays the electrons are fired away with a considerable energy, which may be measured in a variety of ways, for example, by observing their deflection in a magnetic field. In accordance with the general ideas of quantum theory, which we discuss in Chapter **VII**, only certain well-defined values of energy can occur in nuclei. Indeed, α-particles and γ-rays are always emitted from nuclei with well-defined, discrete energy values; the same might, therefore, have been expected in the case of β-rays. Instead of this, it was found that electrons emitted from the nuclei of a given isotope have a continuous distribution of energies, from zero up to a certain maximum value. The graph on Fig. 4 shows a typical energy distribution of β-rays; the horizontal scale gives the energy, and the vertical scale the number of electrons which are emitted with the given energy. It is seen that there is a continuous distribution in which all energies are represented, instead of only certain discrete values. The problem is, however, not only of the observation of a continuous instead of a discrete spectrum, but also of an unaccountable loss of energy. It is often possible to calculate from other data the amount of energy which has been released during the β-transformation, and which should have appeared as the energy of the emitted β-rays. Actually, in every case where such calculation is made, the total energy released is found to be equal to the upper limit of the spectrum, and as seen from the graph of Fig. 4 all electrons are emitted with less energy than this value. The question then arises, what has happened to the remainder of the energy? The cardinal law of physics, the law of conservation of energy, appears to have broken down in the case of β-decay.

Another law which appears to have broken down is that of the conservation of angular momentum, or spin. All elementary particles behave as if they had a spinning motion with a well-defined angular momentum, and in all nuclear reactions the total value of the angular momentum remains unchanged. In the process of β-decay, however, there is no such balance, some angular momentum appears to have been lost.

In order to save the two principal laws of physics a new particle had to be invented. This was done by the Swiss physicist Pauli who proposed the neutrino hypothesis in 1933. According to this hypothesis, when a neutron changes into a proton, or *vice versa*, in addition to the electron yet another particle is created, the neutrino. This particle has no mass, or at least a mass small compared with that of the electron, and it has no electric charge. For these reasons it does not interact with matter through which it passes and consequently it is practically impossible to observe it. Nevertheless, it performs a very important function: it takes away part of the energy available in the $\beta$-decay, the total energy of the decay being shared between the electron and the neutrino. In this way the continuous energy spectrum of the $\beta$-rays can be explained. Similarly, by assigning to the neutrino the same spin as the other elementary particles have, the total angular momentum can be conserved. Although the neutrino was originally invented only to preserve the conservation laws, it turned out to be of very great theoretical value. By using the neutrino hypothesis, Fermi was able to put forward in 1934 a complete theory of $\beta$-decay, which explained quantitatively both the shape of the spectrum and the total probability of the decay. Later, some indirect evidence of emission of neutrinos from nuclei became known, so that the existence of this hypothetic particle seems to be well supported.

## Mesons

It was stated above that the nuclear forces are exchange forces in which neutrons change into protons and *vice versa*. In the light of the neutrino hypothesis it becomes necessary to assume that in each such process two particles, an electron and a neutrino, are exchanged. For example, in the interaction between a neutron and a proton, a neutron changes into a proton with the emission of an electron and neutrino; the latter two are then captured by the proton which is turned into a neutron.

On the basis of Fermi's theory of the $\beta$-decay, it is possible to calculate the strength of the forces which keep the nucleus together. On the other hand, it is possible to measure these forces directly, from observations on collisions between protons and neutrons. A comparison of these two procedures has revealed an enormous gap. The forces calculated on the basis of Fermi's theory of $\beta$-decay were found to be some thousands of times smaller than the values obtained in collision experiments. Thus another serious conflict emerged between theory and experiment.

In an attempt to remove this difficulty the Japanese physicist Yukawa put forward in 1935 the hypothesis that the exchange of protons into neutrons does not take place as suggested above, by the emission of an electron and neutrino, but by the emission of another particle, of mass several hundred times greater than that of the electron. This particle was given the name meson, as its mass is intermediate between that of the proton and electron. The main virtue of the meson is that it is a much stronger 'glue' than the electron to keep the nucleons together, and Yukawa has shown that the postulation of its existence will remove the divergence between theory and experiment. The emission of $\beta$-rays from the nucleus would then be a two-stage process: first, a neutron changes into a proton and a negative meson, and in the next stage the meson breaks up spontaneously into an electron and a neutrino. Similarly, the emission of a positron from the nucleus would occur in two stages: the change of a proton into a neutron and a positive meson, followed by the break up of the latter into a positron and neutrino.

Yukawa's hypothesis did not receive initially much attention, but several years later a particle having the properties predicted by him was indeed discovered experimentally. As in the case of the positron a few years earlier, the meson was discovered in cosmic radiation by a group of American scientists. They observed tracks of cosmic rays in the cloud chamber which could only be made by particles of unit charge and of mass about two hundred times the electron mass. Both positive and negative mesons were observed and it was also found that they were not stable but broke up spontaneously within a few millionths of a s ·ond, changing into electrons and neutrinos.

After this discovery it was thought that the mesons from the cosmic radiation were just the particles needed to account for the magnitude of the nuclear forces. Soon, however, it became clear that this was not so. It was found that the cosmic ray mesons very rarely interacted with nuclei, they could pass through large thicknesses of matter with hardly any absorption. If so, they could not be expected to play an important role in binding the nucleus together. The old problem of the nuclear forces still remained unexplained.

It was not until 1947 that a satisfactory solution was found. In that year Powell and his collaborators at Bristol discovered another, heavier type of meson. They employed the photographic emulsion technique which makes use of the fact that the passage of a charged particle through an emulsion renders the grains along its path developable; after processing the emulsion the path is revealed as a row of black grains which can be seen through a microscope. From the length of the track and the density of grains in it the mass and energy of the particle can often be determined. Powell exposed photographic plates to cosmic rays at high altitudes and found in them a number of events which could leave no doubt that they were due to the passage of particles of intermediate mass which decay after a short time into other intermediate particles, the latter being identical with those previously observed in cosmic radiations. To distinguish between the various types of mesons he suggested the name $\mu$-meson for the lighter particles and $\pi$-meson for the newly discovered heavier type. The photograph of Plate V, which was obtained by Powell later with more sensitive emulsions, shows the successive transformations of the mesons. The first track is due to that of a $\pi$-meson; it is seen that the density of the grains increases from bottom to top, indicating that the particle was moving in this direction. The $\pi$-meson then came to rest and gave rise to a $\mu$ meson, which then produced its own track until it came to rest and in turn decayed into an electron. Further investigations with $\pi$-mesons have shown that they interact very strongly with nuclei and indeed behave like the particles predicted by Yukawa. It must, therefore, be assumed that it is the $\pi$-meson which keeps the proton and neutron together in the nucleus; this particle is also called the pion.

The initial investigations on mesons had to be carried out with those present in the cosmic radiations, as no other source of mesons was known. Later, however, it became possible to produce mesons artificially in the large accelerating machines. If a beam of, say, protons of a very high energy is made to strike a light element, a copious emission of mesons is observed. In fact, the main object of the colossal accelerators which have been developed in recent years (see Chapter III) was to produce mesons of various types. It is thus possible nowadays to obtain intense beams of both $\pi$-mesons and $\mu$-mesons, and this has greatly facilitated the study of their properties.

We know now that there are three types of pions, positive, negative and neutral. The mass of the positive or negative pion is 273 electron masses, while the neutral $\pi$-meson has a mass 264 electron masses. All $\pi$-mesons are very short-lived; the mean life of the charged pion is about $10^{-8}$ second, while that of the neutral pion is even shorter, about $10^{-14}$ second. At the end of their life charged $\pi$-mesons decay into $\mu$-mesons and neutrinos; a neutral $\pi$-meson just disappears, its mass being transformed into energy which appears as two $\gamma$-rays.

Of $\mu$-mesons, or muons, only two types are known, a positive and a negative one; both have the same mass which is 207 electron masses. Their mean life is $2 \times 10^{-6}$ second; a negative $\mu$-meson breaks up into an electron and two neutrinos, a positive $\mu$-meson into a positron and two neutrinos. It is necessary to postulate the emission of two neutrinos at each $\mu$-meson decay in order to maintain the balance of angular momentum. Unlike the $\pi$-mesons which are essential for the theory of nuclear forces, the role played by $\mu$-mesons is not yet clear.

Later investigations have revealed the existence of other mesons of still higher masses. As usual, such particles are first discovered in cosmic radiations, until the development of still bigger accelerators catches up for a while. Among those mesons whose existence was definitely established and which have since been produced artificially are the so-called $\tau$-mesons, which have a mass 967 times the electron mass. Two types of $\tau$-mesons are known, positive and negative. They decay mainly into three $\pi$-mesons, *i.e.* into two positive and one negative or two negative and one positive. The properties of other types of mesons of about the same mass – they have the collective name K-mesons – are not yet well known. There is also definite evidence that particles of masses greater than that of the proton are present in cosmic radiation. Such particles can no longer be called mesons and they were given the name of hyperons; several types of these are known, *i.e.* $\Lambda$-, $\Sigma$-, and $\Omega$-particles. The artificial production of hyperons in accelerators has been reported recently.

*Elementary particles?*

We have gone a long way from the simple picture of a universe which required only three elementary particles to build up all matter. At the moment at least sixteen elementary particles are known and the existence of as many again is possible. Our present-day knowledge of elementary particles is summarized in Table I in which all particles are listed together with their charge, mass, lifetime and mode of decay. Since all the charged particles carry one unit of electrical charge only the sign is given. The mass is given in units of the electron mass. The last column gives the collective names which were given to groups of particles.

One particle whose existence has been predicted but has not yet been observed is the negative proton which would be the counterpart of the positive proton, just as the positron is to the electron. Like the positron such an anti-proton would have a very brief existence, since it would soon be annihilated in a collision with a proton.*

The great multiplicity of these particles is highly unsatisfactory and raises the question of what we really mean by an elementary particle. Originally the name was applied to the four elements, fire, earth, air and water. Later, it was thought that the atom of each chemical element was an elementary particle. Then the term was limited to three only, proton, neutron and electron; it has now been extended to over twenty particles, and still more may yet be discovered. Is there really a need for so many units of matter, or is this multiplicity of particles an expression of our total ignorance of the true nature of the ultimate structure of matter? It has been suggested that some of the particles are really a combination of others, or that a particle in an excited state may appear to us like a separate particle. It is more likely, however, that an entirely new approach to the whole problem is necessary. At the moment, despite the remarkable progress made in nuclear physics, the riddle of elementary particles still remains unsolved.

* Since this was written the existence of the negative proton has been established experimentally.

## TABLE I
## ELEMENTARY PARTICLES

| Particle | Symbol | Charge | Mass | Mean life (seconds) | Mode of decay | Group |
|---|---|---|---|---|---|---|
| Neutrino | $\nu$ | 0 | 0 | stable | | Leptons |
| Electron | $e^-$ | − | 1 | stable | | |
| Positron | $e^+$ | + | 1 | stable | | |
| Positive $\mu$-meson | $\mu^+$ | + | 207 | $2 \cdot 2 \times 10^{-6}$ | $\mu^+ \rightarrow e^+ + 2\nu$ | L-mesons |
| Negative $\mu$-meson | $\mu^-$ | − | 207 | $2 \cdot 2 \times 10^{-6}$ | $\mu^- \rightarrow e^- + 2\nu$ | |
| Positive $\pi$-meson | $\pi^+$ | + | 273 | $2 \cdot 6 \times 10^{-8}$ | $\pi^+ \rightarrow \mu^+ + \nu$ | |
| Negative $\pi$-meson | $\pi^-$ | − | 273 | $2 \cdot 6 \times 10^{-8}$ | $\pi^- \rightarrow \mu^- + \nu$ | |
| Neutral $\pi$-meson | $\pi^\circ$ | 0 | 264 | $5 \times 10^{-15}$ | $\pi^\circ \rightarrow 2\gamma$ | |
| Positive $\tau$-meson | $\tau^+$ | + | 967 | $10^{-8}$ | $\tau^+ \rightarrow \pi^+ + \pi^- + \pi^+$ | K-mesons |
| Negative $\tau$-meson | $\tau^-$ | − | 967 | $10^{-8}$ | $\tau^- \rightarrow \pi^+ + \pi^- + \pi^-$ | |
| $\theta$-meson | $\theta^\circ$ | 0 | 965 | $2 \times 10^{-10}$ | $\theta^\circ \rightarrow \pi^+ + \pi^-$ | |
| $\chi$-meson | $\chi^\pm$ | ++ | ~1000 | ~$10^{-9}$ | | |
| K-meson | $K^\pm$ | ++ | ~1000 | ~$10^{-9}$ | | |
| Proton | p | + | 1836 | stable | | Nucleons |
| Neutron | n | 0 | 1838·5 | 750 | | |
| Anti-proton | $p^-$ | − | 1836 | | | |
| Neutral $\Lambda$-particle | $\Lambda^\circ$ | 0 | 2182 | $3 \cdot 7 \times 10^{-10}$ | $\Lambda^\circ \rightarrow p + \pi^-$ | Hyperons |
| Positive $\Sigma$-particle | $\Sigma^+$ | + | 2339 | $3 \times 10^{-10}$ | $\Sigma^+ \rightarrow n + \pi^+ \ or \rightarrow p + \pi^\circ$ | |
| Negative $\Sigma$-particle | $\Sigma^-$ | − | 2339 | $3 \times 10^{-10}$ | $\Sigma^- \rightarrow n + \pi^-$ | |
| Negative $\Omega$-particle | $\Omega^-$ | − | 2660 | $10^{-10}$ | $\Omega^- \rightarrow \Lambda^\circ + \pi^-$ | |

# CHAPTER II

## *The atom breaks up*

### *The radiations from radioactive elements*

As already mentioned in Chapter I, soon after the discovery in 1895 of radioactivity, *i.e.* the spontaneous emission of radiations from uranium and several other heavy elements, it was observed that these radiations consisted of three distinct types, which for brevity and convenience were termed α-, β- and γ-rays. The analysis of the radiations into the various groups can best be effected by using a magnetic field. In such a field charged particles are deflected, positive particles in one direction and negative in the opposite direction, while uncharged radiation remains unaffected.

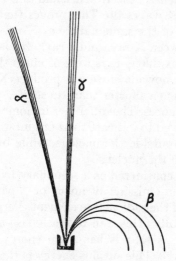

FIG. 5. *Deflection of α-, β- and γ-rays by a magnetic field.*

Fig. 5 shows the result which would be obtained if a strong magnet were brought near a radioactive substance in such a way that the north pole was above the plane of the paper and the south pole beneath it. It is seen that one group of rays is deflected slightly to the left, which means that these must be particles carrying a positive electric charge. This group is called 'α-particles'. The fact that they are all deflected uniformly indicates that they are all emitted with the same energy. Another group of rays is seen to be much more strongly deflected to the right, which indicates that they are negatively charged particles. They are spread out widely, which proves that the particles are emitted with various energies. This group was given the name 'β-rays' and, as we know already, they are fast electrons.

Finally, the third group which passes through the field undeviated are called 'γ-rays'. The fact that they are unaffected by the magnetic field may mean either that they are particles with no electric charge or a pure wave, an electromagnetic radiation. Later it became possible to demonstrate directly that γ-rays show the phenomena of interference and diffraction, much in the same way as light waves do. This proves that they are electromagnetic waves, of the same nature as X-rays. In fact, there is no difference between X-rays and γ-rays. Initially the distinction between them was that γ-rays were of much shorter wavelength than X-rays, but nowadays we can produce X-rays of the same wavelength and even shorter than those of γ-rays emitted from radioactive substances. The difference in nomenclature has, however, been preserved to indicate their origin: we call X-rays those originating from outside the nucleus, while by γ-rays we mean rays coming from the nucleus.

γ-rays may be considered as a secondary by-product of radioactive decay. The emission of an α- or β-particle results in a transformation of the radioactive element. Very often the isotope produced as a result of this transformation is formed in an excited state, which means that it has more energy than the normal nucleus would have. This surplus energy is then got rid of in the form of electromagnetic radiation, which in this case we call γ-rays. It is a process similar to that occurring in the atom when it is in an 'excited state'; the return to the normal state is accompanied by the emission of radiation in the form of light. Since the energies contained in the nucleus are about a million times greater than those involving the outer shell of the atom, the $\gamma$-rays emitted from radioactive substances have an average energy about a million times greater than the energy carried by light waves.

## *The $\alpha$-particle*

From the point of view of the role played in elucidating the structure of the nucleus the most important turned out to be the $\alpha$-particles. It was Rutherford who very early and intuitively recognized the $\alpha$-particles as the most powerful tool for probing the structure of the atom, and most of his work was concerned with this particle. Using methods similar to those described in the case of electrons, *i.e.* deflection in electric and magnetic fields, Rutherford was able to measure the velocity of the $\alpha$-particles and the ratio of their charge to mass. In other experiments in which the total charge carried by a known number of $\alpha$-particles was measured he was able to determine the charge of each $\alpha$-particle.

These experiments proved that the $\alpha$-particles emitted from all radioactive substances are identical in nature: their charge is positive and twice the charge carried by an electron, and their mass is four times that of the hydrogen atom. According to our present-day views we realize immediately that the $\alpha$-particle must be the nucleus of the helium atom, and composed of two protons and two neutrons. In those days, however, nothing was known about the nucleus, and the conclusion that an atom of one chemical element, helium, is emitted from the atom of another chemical element, say, radium, seemed so revolutionary that more direct evidence about its nature was necessary before it would be accepted. This piece of evidence was provided by Rutherford in the following experiment (Fig. 6). A quantity of radon, a radioactive gas, was compressed into the tube T which had walls thin enough to allow the $\alpha$-particles emitted from radon to penetrate into the outer tube O. This latter tube was very thoroughly evacuated at the beginning of the experiment when a spectroscopic analysis showed no traces of helium in it.

After leaving the radon for several days it was found that some gas accumulated in the outer tube; this gas was then compressed, by bringing up the level of the mercury, into the discharge tube D, where its content could be analysed by observing the spectrum of light emitted after an electric discharge was produced. The complete spectrum of helium was observed, and thus direct proof was obtained both of the identity of α-particles with helium and of the production of helium from radon.

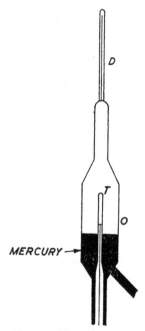

Fig. 6. *Experiment to prove identity of α-particles.*

As already mentioned, the α-particles from a given radioactive isotope are all emitted with the same energy. This can be verified by deflecting the beam of α-particles in a magnetic field and measuring their energies directly, or more simply, although indirectly, by putting a source of α-particles into a cloud chamber and taking a photograph of their tracks. Such a photograph is shown in Plate VII. Each of the white lines represents a track of an α-particle. It is seen that the tracks are almost all straight lines, which indicates that the α-particle can generally pass through a thickness of air without changing its direction. The tracks end abruptly, and the distance travelled by an α-particle is called its range. In the photograph two definite ranges are seen; in air at atmospheric pressure the range of one group would be 4·8 cm. and of the other 8·6 cm. There are two ranges because the source contained in this case two radioactive elements called Thorium C and Thorium C', each of which emits α-particles of a definite range. The range depends on the energy; the higher the energy of the particle the further it can penetrate. From the measurement of the range it is possible to determine the energy of the particle.

In nuclear physics energies are measured in electron-volts rather than in the usual units, ergs. If a proton or an electron are accelerated in an electric field they acquire an energy which is proportional to the potential across the field. We define the electron-volt as the amount of energy gained by an electron or a proton in passing through a potential difference of one volt. An α-particle, being doubly charged, will acquire double the energy in passing through the same difference of potential. In these units the energies of the two groups of α-particles from Thorium C and C' are 6·1 and 8·8 million electron-volts (MeV). Among the various natural radioactive elements the α-particles from Thorium C' have the highest energy; the lowest, 4·0 MeV, are from thorium-232.

## Radioactive transformations

Having established that radioactive substances emit spontaneously either helium nuclei or electrons, we may ask, what is the result of such emission? Rutherford and Soddy were the first to investigate this problem, but we shall consider it in the light of our present knowledge of the structure of the nucleus. We shall start with radium, which decays with the emission of an α-particle. This element has an atomic number 88 and mass number 226, which means that its nucleus is composed of 88 protons and 138 neutrons. If an α-particle is emitted from it, *i.e.* 2 protons and 2 neutrons, the remaining element will have atomic number 86 and mass number 222. In the Periodic Table element number 86 belongs to the group of inert gases (helium, neon, argon, krypton and xenon) and is called radon. Thus, as a result of the emission of an α-particle radium has changed into radon; we have here the first case of transmutation of elements. This process continues with radon, which also emits an α-particle. The result of this decay is the formation of an element called polonium of atomic number 84 and mass number 218. Before the existence of isotopes was established this particular substance was given the name Radium A. Radium A again decays by α-particle emission, producing element of atomic number 82 and mass number 214, *i.e.* lead. This isotope of lead of mass 214 was called Radium B. Radium B is found to decay by β-emission. As we know already, the emission of an electron is due to the transformation of a neutron into a proton. Since the masses of a proton and a neutron are approximately the same, the element produced in the transformation will have the same mass number 214, but since one of the neutrons has changed into a proton the charge of the nucleus has increased by one and consequently the atomic number of the product will be 83, which is that of bismuth. We find thus that the product of decay of Radium B is an isotope of bismuth which was called Radium C.

In a similar fashion we can follow the successive transformations of all the radioactive substances. Each time an α-particle is emitted the atomic number is decreased by two and the mass number by four; at each β-emission the mass number remains unchanged and the atomic number is increased by one. All radioactive substances found in nature among the heaviest elements can in this way be arranged into family trees, and it has been found that they form three separate radioactive series.

Apart from its atomic number and mass number each radioactive substance is characterized by the rate at which its atoms break up. In a given radioactive substance not all of its atoms break up at the same time; some decay after a very short time, others may exist for a long time. It is a process governed by chance, but if the substance contains a very large number of unstable atoms a simple statistical law is observed, namely that

in equal intervals of time equal fractions of all atoms present
undergo disintegration. As a measure of the rate of decay one
usually takes the period of time in which half of all the radioactive atoms disintegrate. This period is called the half-value
period or simply the half-life and is a characteristic property of
the given radioactive isotope. The graph of Fig. 7 represents the

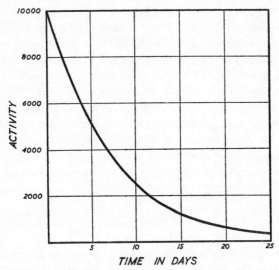

FIG. 7. *Decay of activity of radioactive substance.*

rate of decay of a radioactive substance; the vertical scale gives
the number of atoms which have survived up to the time given
on the horizontal scale. This graph refers to the radioactive isotope Radium E, which has a half-life of 5 days. Starting off with
10,000 atoms, we find that after 5 days 5,000 atoms are left;
after another 5 days there are 2,500 survivors; after another
5 days 1,250, and so on. This type of variation is called an
exponential function and is characteristic for any process which
occurs at random; in the case of radioactive disintegration this
means that the decay of any one atom is independent of the fate
of any other atom.

The radioactive substances occurring in nature have half-lives covering an enormous range, from thousands of millions of years to a fraction of a millionth of a second. The shortest half-life, $3 \times 10^{-7}$ second, is of Thorium C', the isotope which emits the fastest $\alpha$-particles; the longest half-life, $1.4 \times 10^{10}$ years, is that of thorium-232, which emits the least energetic $\alpha$-particles.

The radioactive intensity of a given substance depends not on the total number of atoms in the substance but on the number of atoms which break up in a given time. A small amount of a substance of a short half-life may show a stronger radioactivity than a large amount of a long-lived substance, because in the former more rays are given off every second; the effect of the latter will of course last longer. The number of atoms of a given substance which disintegrate every second is called the activity and is measured in a unit called the curie. It is nearly equal to the activity of one gramme of radium, and is the quantity of a radioactive substance in which 37,000 million atoms break up every second. The curie turned out to be a very large unit and for this reason smaller units. the millicurie (one-thousandth of a curie) and the microcurie (one-millionth of a curie) are often used.

### The radioactive series

As already stated, all radioactive isotopes among the heavy elements can be arranged in three series, which are shown in Fig. 8. The uranium series starts off with the isotope uranium-238, which used to be called Uranium I and which has a very long half-life of $4.5 \times 10^9$ years. It emits $\alpha$-particles and is then transformed into an isotope of thorium of mass number 234, called Uranium $X_1$. This has a half-life of only 24 days; it emits $\beta$-rays, and is transformed into an isotope of protactinium-234 called Uranium $X_2$, which has an even shorter half-life of $1.1$ minutes. A second $\beta$-decay follows resulting in the production of another isotope of uranium of mass 234, called Uranium II. This sequence illustrates how a large number of isotopes can occur among a few elements: after one $\alpha$- and two $\beta$-transformations we return to the same element. After Uranium II there is a sequence of two $\alpha$-disintegrations leading to the formation of radium, which has a half-life of 1,622 years. The sequence from

radium to Radium C has already been discussed. An interesting
phenomenon occurs with this isotope. It can decay either by α-
or β-emission. In the first case, the product Radium C″ emits a
β-ray turning into an isotope of lead, Radium D. In the second
case, the product Radium C′ emits an α-particle and is transformed into the same isotope, Radium D. Two other examples
of such branching occur in Radium A and Radium E. Finally,
the series ends with the formation of an isotope of lead of mass
number 206. This isotope was found to undergo no further transmutation; it is a non-radioactive, stable isotope.

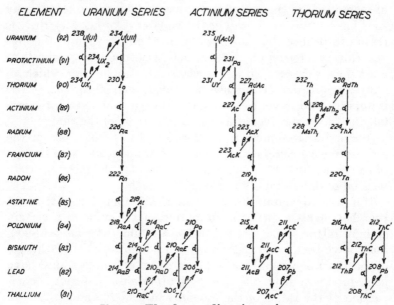

FIG. 8. *The three radioactive series.*

The second series, which is called the actinium series, starts off
with an isotope of uranium of mass number 235, called Actino-
Uranium. It has a half-life $7 \times 10^8$ years and passes through a
somewhat similar series of transformations, ending again in a
stable isotope of lead of mass number 207.

Finally, the thorium series starts off with an isotope of thorium of mass 232, which has the very long half-life of $1 \cdot 4 \times 10^{10}$ years. As in the case of the uranium series there follow a number of transformations through successive α- and β-decays, ending finally in the formation of another stable isotope of lead, of mass number 208.

It will now be clear why we observe in nature isotopes of short half-lives, of the order of days, minutes or even fractions of seconds. These isotopes are being continually produced from their parents, which in turn are produced from the main parents of the three series, uranium-238, uranium-235 and thorium-232. All these three isotopes have very long half-lives, of the same order of magnitude as the age of the universe. This is the reason why they have survived. As will be shown later (Chapter XI), there is reason to believe that at one stage in the formation of the universe a very large number of radioactive isotopes, far greater than exist now, were created in a nuclear catastrophe from which all matter originated. If this had happened, then all the short-lived isotopes would have decayed since and only the ones with very long half-lives survived; these are the parents of the three radio-active series. It follows from this that the proportions of the radioactive elements which occur now are dependent on the age of the earth. In fact, this forms the basis for the most accurate method of determining the age of the earth.

If a mineral contains, say, uranium-238, then during the time that has elapsed since the formation of the mineral a certain amount of the stable end-product of uranium-238, *i.e.* lead-206, must have been produced, and this amount depends on the age of the mineral. Similarly, a certain amount of lead-207 must have been produced from the decay of uranium-235. From a comparison of the ratios of the amounts of lead-206 and 207, with the ratios of the amounts of uranium-238 and 235, the age of the mineral can be accurately determined.

Apart from the 41 elements forming the members of the three radioactive families, there are a few isolated radioactive isotopes occurring among other elements. These are isotopes of potassium, rubidium, lanthanum, samarium, lutecium and rhenium. All of these are characterised by very long half lives of the order of the age of the earth. The most interesting of these is potassium-40, which is the lightest of all natural radioactive elements and is the only radioactive constituent of the human body. The total activity of radio-potassium in the body amounts to only 0·1 microcuries.

### Stable and unstable nuclei

So far we have described the main features of radioactivity as elucidated from a great many observations, but we have not yet attempted to find the reason for this phenomenon. Why are some elements unstable? Why do some substances emit $\alpha$-particles, while others emit $\beta$-rays? In order to find an answer to these questions we must turn for a moment to stable nuclei.

We have already explained how, by means of the mass spectrometer, it is possible to analyse the isotopic composition of a given element. Such studies have shown that some elements, those with odd atomic numbers, have a very small number of isotopes, either one or two, while even elements have on the whole larger numbers of isotopes, up to 10. Altogether among the 81 stable elements occurring in nature there is a total of 275 stable isotopes. Fig. 9 shows a chart of all isotopes occurring in nature. The horizontal scale gives the number of protons, and the vertical scale the number of neutrons. Each square represents one isotope; the squares lying in one vertical line represent isotopes of the same chemical element. The stable isotopes are indicated by open squares; the radioactive isotopes by full squares.

It will be seen that in light elements the number of protons is approximately equal to the number of neutrons, but as we go over to heavier elements the number of neutrons increases faster than the number of protons. In very heavy elements the ratio of the number of neutrons to protons is about 1·6. It is easy to explain the reason for this. Apart from the attractive nuclear forces acting between the nucleons there are also the electrostatic repulsive forces between the protons. Since the specific nuclear forces have a very short range they can only act between nucleons which are in the immediate vicinity of each other. The total attractive force will, therefore, be proportional to the number of particles in the nucleons. On the other hand, the electric forces of repulsion between the protons have a long range, which means that each proton repels every other proton in the nucleus; the total repulsive force is thus approximately proportional to the *square* of the number of protons. As the number of protons in a nucleus increases, the repulsive forces increase faster than the attractive forces, and in order to restore the balance more particles are needed to provide attractive forces. Hence there must be more neutrons than protons.

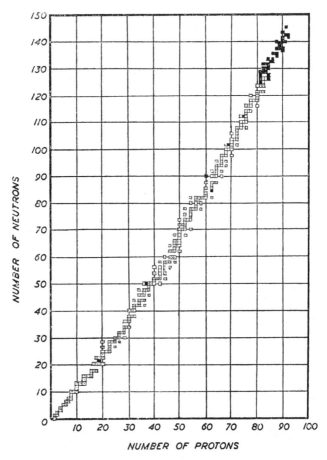

FIG. 9. *Chart of isotopes occurring in nature.*

It follows from this argument that only nuclei in which the ratio of protons to neutrons lies within certain limits can be stable. In fact it will be noticed that in the chart of Fig. 9 all stable isotopes occupy a very narrow region of the graph. What would happen if a nucleus were formed which lay above or below this region of stability? Such a nucleus would be unstable and would tend to undergo a transformation leading it into a more stable form. Such transformation would be the conversion of a proton into a neutron or *vice versa*. We have already learned that such conversion can take place and that an electron and a neutrino are created in the process. Since electrons cannot exist in nuclei they are immediately ejected. We observe then the phenomenon of β-decay. We can understand now why some isotopes are radioactive and undergo a β-decay, but we have still to explain α-decay; why do some elements which are apparently stable against β-decay break up with the emission of an α-particle? This appears to be particularly strange as the α-particle is not an elementary particle but an aggregate of four nucleons. In order to explain this it is necessary to consider the energy balance within the nucleus.

*Binding energy*

When a nucleus is transformed into another, either by α- or β-decay, some energy is released in the process, which is taken up as the energy of motion of the α- or the β-particle, with any surplus appearing as γ-rays. As we have seen, the energy released from the nucleus may be quite high – of the order of millions of electron-volts – and the question may be asked where does this energy come from? In order to answer this question we must look more closely at the values of the atomic weights of isotopes. As already mentioned the atomic weights of all isotopes are very nearly whole numbers. Very nearly but not exactly, and this small difference turns out to be of great importance, so great that special techniques, mainly based on the mass spectrometer, have been devised to measure the atomic weights with the highest possible degree of accuracy. Table II gives the exact values, as far as we know them, of the atomic weights of several isotopes of the light elements.

c

TABLE II

ATOMIC WEIGHTS OF SOME LIGHT
ISOTOPES

| *Isotope* | *Symbol* | *Atomic weight* |
|---|---|---|
| Neutron | $^1$n | 1·008982 |
| Hydrogen | $^1$H | 1·008142 |
| Deuterium | $^2$D | 2·014735 |
| Tritium | $^3$T | 3·016997 |
| Helium-3 | $^3$He | 3·016977 |
| Helium-4 | $^4$He | 4·003873 |
| Lithium-6 | $^6$Li | 6·017021 |
| Lithium-7 | $^7$Li | 7·018223 |
| Beryllium-9 | $^9$Be | 9·015043 |
| Carbon-12 | $^{12}$C | 12·003804 |
| Nitrogen-14 | $^{14}$N | 14·007515 |
| Oxygen-16 | $^{16}$O | 16·000000 |
| Oxygen-17 | $^{17}$O | 17·004533 |

Let us consider the case of the α-particle. Since it is the nucleus of helium, and is made up of 2 protons and 2 neutrons, we might have expected that the weight of the helium nucleus would be equal to the sum of the weights of 2 protons and 2 neutrons. Actually this is not so. If we add up the atomic weights of 2 hydrogen atoms and 2 neutrons we obtain 4·034248, while the atomic weight of helium is 4·003873. We find then that the weight of the helium nucleus is smaller than the atomic weight of its constituents by about 0·030 units of atomic weight. (It is quite legitimate to use atomic weights when dealing with nuclei, because the extra weight of the electrons in the atom must balance on both sides of the equation.) What has happened to the missing weight? The answer is that it has been converted into energy in accordance with Einstein's principle of the equivalence of mass and energy. It is well known that in certain chemical reactions energy is released in the form of heat, and the amount of heat released is a measure of the stability of the given compound; because if we wanted to break up the compound we would have to deliver to it the same amount of energy that was released during its formation. Similarly, when a nucleus is formed from its constituents some energy is released, and this energy release is a measure of the stability of the given nucleus; for in order to break up the nucleus one would have to supply it with the same amount of energy. This is the reason why the compound nucleus weighs less than its constituents, and the difference, or mass defect, represents the binding energy of the nucleus. In the case of the helium nucleus the binding energy is 0·030 units of atomic weight. It is easy to convert this into energy units, say electron-volts. From Einstein's mass-energy relation it follows that one unit of atomic weight is equivalent to 936 MeV (million electron-volts). The binding energy of the helium nucleus is thus 28 MeV. This is the amount of energy which is released when an $\alpha$-particle is formed; an amount which would have been obtained if a proton had been accelerated through a difference of potential of 28 million volts. This gives an idea of the order of magnitude of the forces acting in the nucleus. This very high binding energy shows that the helium nucleus is a very stable structure.

In a similar fashion we can work out the binding energies for all other isotopes, and if these are plotted against the mass number we obtain a very interesting graph (Fig. 10). Actually, the graph of Fig. 10 shows not the total binding energy of the nucleus but the binding energy divided by the number of nucleons; it gives, therefore, the average amount of energy necessary to remove one particle from the nucleus. As is seen, the binding energy per nucleon starts off with low values in light elements, increases very rapidly, then flattens out and decreases again for heavier elements. In the region of light elements the variation is not as smooth as the continuous curve would lead one to believe. In fact some isotopes, like $^4$He, $^{12}$C or $^{16}$O, lie well above the curve, which means that they are particularly stable structures.

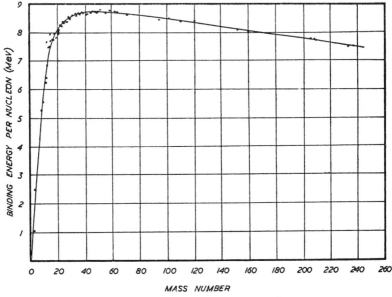

FIG. 10. *Binding-energy per nucleon.*

There are two interesting features of this curve. First, for a large number of isotopes, with mass numbers from about 30 to about 120, the curve changes very little and gives a practically constant binding energy per nucleon of about 8·5 MeV. This means that for most nuclei the binding energy is proportional to the number of particles in it. This result is a strong argument in favour of the short-range character of the nuclear forces; for if they were of long-range, like electrical or gravitational forces, each nucleon would have interacted with every other and the total binding energy might have been expected to be nearly proportional to the square of the mass numbers. Secondly, the binding energy curve has a maximum in the region of medium-weight elements. This means that these elements of medium weight are the most stable ones. If we started with a very heavy element and split it into two, then some energy would be released, corresponding to the difference in the binding energy for heavy and medium elements. Similarly, if two light elements were fused together to form a medium weight element, there would again be a release of energy. Both these methods have actually been used in order to obtain nuclear energy for practical purposes, as will be discussed in the following chapters.

At the moment we are concerned with the problem of $\alpha$-decay which occurs in the very heavy elements. In this region the average binding energy per nucleon is about 7·5 MeV; but from the slope of the graph (Fig. 10) we find that the binding energy per *additional* particle is only about 5·5 MeV. This means that if we wanted to take away one proton or one neutron from a heavy nucleus we would have to supply the nucleus with 5·5 MeV. Therefore, if we wanted to take away two protons and two neutrons separately we would have to supply the nucleus with a total energy of about 22 million electron-volts. On the other hand, we know that the binding energy of an $\alpha$-particle is 28 million electron-volts. Consequently, if these four particles came out not individually but combined as an $\alpha$-particle, we would have a net gain of 6 million electron-volts, because we would have to put in 22 MeV and would have gained 28 MeV. Thus, although such a nucleus may be stable with regard to the emission of a proton or a neutron, yet it will be unstable with regard to the emission of an $\alpha$-particle, because each time an $\alpha$-particle is emitted we shall have a positive release of energy of about 6 MeV. This is the reason why heavy elements are unstable and break up with the emission of $\alpha$-particles, which have an energy between 4 and 9 MeV.

### Theory of $\alpha$-decay

We have just shown that heavy nuclei are unstable because energy is released if they break up with the emission of $\alpha$-particles. If so, the question may be asked why do they not break up instantaneously? Why does it take some nuclei many years to break up? In order to answer this we must discuss the variation of the potential energy inside and around the nucleus.

The positively charged protons inside the nucleus exert a repulsive force on any approaching particle with a positive charge; it is known from elementary physics that this force of repulsion increases as the distance between the charges decreases. A repulsive force corresponds to a positive potential energy, and the stronger the force the greater the potential energy. If, therefore,

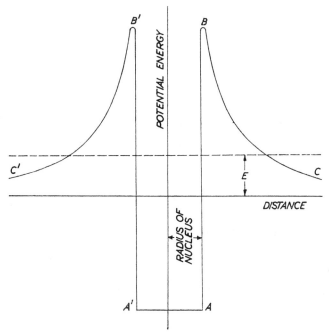

FIG. 11. *Potential field around a nucleus as seen by a charged particle.*

the potential energy between two positively charged particles is plotted as a function of the distance between them, a curve is obtained of the form BC in Fig. 11. In this graph the horizontal scale gives the distance of a charged particle from the centre of the nucleus, and the vertical scale the potential energy of the system. It is seen that if the particle approached the nucleus from a distance, the potential energy is increasing, indicating a larger repulsive force. But at the point B the particle reached the boundary of the nucleus and suddenly came under the action of the very strong attractive nuclear forces. These attractive forces are much stronger than the repulsive force, and consequently the potential energy suddenly drops to a large negative value.

The part of the curve BAA'B' represents the shape of the potential energy inside the nucleus; it is of the shape of a deep well. Since we still do not know the nature of the nuclear forces, we cannot calculate the exact shape of the curve inside the well, but this does not really matter for our present argument; for simplicity, it is shown as a rectangular well. The important point is that there exists a so-called potential barrier around the nucleus due to the action of the electric repulsive forces. Any charged particle coming from outside has to go over the top of the potential barrier in order to enter the nucleus, *i.e.* it must have an energy at least equal to the height of the barrier at B. Similarly, a particle inside the nucleus must cross the barrier in order to escape from it. It should be pointed out that the term barrier is used only in a figurative sense. There is no real barrier round the nucleus, but the electrical forces round the nucleus are such that if they were replaced by mechanical forces they would have to be represented by a barrier. The height of the potential barrier depends on the charge of the nucleus and on its radius; for a heavy nucleus it is of the order of 25 million electron-volts. As was shown before, an α-particle, if it could escape from the nucleus, would have an excess of energy of about 6 MeV; this value, indicated on the graph by E, is, however, well below the potential barrier, and consequently the particle cannot escape. In fact, according to the laws of classical physics, an α-particle with an energy below the potential barrier would never be able to come out, and so we would not have been able to observe α-radioactivity.

The fact that we do observe the emission of α-particles can only be explained on the basis of modern wave-mechanics, which tells us that radiation often behaves like matter and matter like radiation. According to this the motion of an α-particle can be described as a wave motion, and the space within the potential barrier as a nearly opaque medium, through which the wave has to penetrate. The chance of this penetration is extremely small but it is finite, and like the winning of the treble chance in the pools it may happen if a sufficiently large number of attempts is made. If we think in terms of mechanical analogies, and imagine that there is a real barrier round the nucleus, we can visualize the α-particle inside the well, moving to and fro, and knocking on the wall of the barrier. In the vast majority of these collisions the α-particle is reflected back, but there is a very tiny probability, of the order of one in $10^{14}$, of it penetrating through the barrier and emerging outside. The escape of α-particles is thus a matter of chance, and this is the reason why in a given substance some atoms decay very rapidly, while others exist for a very long time. The probability of escaping through the barrier will, of course, depend on the thickness of the wall to be penetrated. An α-particle which has a high energy will have to go through a thinner barrier and, therefore, its chances of escape are much greater. On the basis of this reasoning we may expect that radioactive substances which send out α-particles of high energy should have a shorter half-life, because the α-particle will be able to get through quickly, while those of a low energy will have a longer half-life. In fact, such a relationship between the energy of the α-particle and the half-life of the substance has been known for a long time and called the 'Geiger-Nuttall Rule'. It was an empirical relationship which was not understood until the theory of α-decay, just outlined, was put forward in 1928. This theory gave not only a qualitative but also a quantitative account of all observed facts. We can, therefore, say that we understand now why the heavy elements decay with the emission of α-particles and why some of them have long and others short half-lives. We also understand why the Periodic Table finishes at the 92nd element; in elements heavier than uranium the α-particles would have had greater energy, and so would have too short half-lives to survive until now.

*Theory of β-decay*

In the case of β-decay, the theory is somewhat different as we deal here not with the emission of nuclear constituents but with the transformation of one nucleon into another, and, resulting from it, the emission of an electron and neutrino. By considering the interaction between the nucleons and the electron and neutrino which are formed during this process, it is possible to calculate the probability of a given nucleus undergoing $\beta$-decay. As was shown in Chapter I, although this theory gave a good qualitative explanation of the experimental facts, the quantitative agreement was not so good, and has led as a result to the necessity of postulating the existence of mesons.

It should now also be clear why $\beta$-emission is observed after $\alpha$-emission among the heavy elements. After several successive $\alpha$-transformations the residual nucleus differs from the original one by the loss of an equal number of neutrons and protons. Since in the region of heavy elements the stable nuclei contain many more neutrons than protons, the loss of the same number of neutrons and protons means that in the new nucleus the ratio of neutrons to protons is higher than that corresponding to a stable nucleus. This can be adjusted by one of the neutrons being transformed into a proton, with the simultaneous emission of an electron and a neutrino. The occurrence of $\beta$-activity following $\alpha$-transformation is thus fully explained.

*Artificial radioactivity*

The chart of isotopes shown on Fig. 9 represents all nuclei which occur in nature in detectable quantities. Among these are the naturally occurring radioactive isotopes, shown by black squares. The remainder are the 275 stable isotopes. Since a very careful search has failed to reveal the presence of any other type of nuclei in nature we may conclude that these are the only stable nuclei. Any other nucleus of a different constitution from those is, therefore, probably unstable.

By means of nuclear disintegrations, which will be discussed in the next chapter, it is now possible to produce nuclei other than those shown in the chart and it has been found that all these are indeed radioactive. In general, those of the artificially produced nuclei which have a higher than normal neutron to proton ratio decay by emission of electrons; those in which this ratio is lower decay by emission of positrons. In many cases an alternative to positron emission is the so-called K-capture, when the nucleus captures one of its orbital electrons, usually the nearest, which is called a K-electron. In a few cases artificially produced α-emitting isotopes have been observed, particularly among the heavy elements. In fact, a fourth radioactive series, which does not exist in nature, has been observed, starting with the artificially produced element neptunium-237 (Fig. 12).

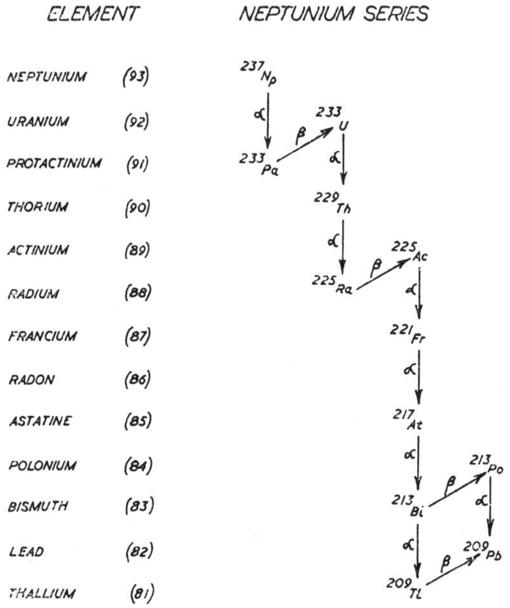

FIG. 12. *The neptunium series.*

Altogether by various means, which will be described later, about 820 radioactive isotopes have now been identified, about three times the number of stable isotopes. All these are shown on the chart of Fig. 13, which is similar to that of Fig. 9; the squares represent stable isotopes and the circles radioactive ones. There is now at least one radioactive isotope known of any of the existing chemical elements, and radioactive isotopes have been produced of those elements which do not occur in nature, such as technetium (43) or promethium (61). In fact, a number of isotopes have been produced of elements heavier than uranium, namely neptunium (93), plutonium (94), americium (95), curium (96), berkelium (97), californium (98), einsteinium (99), fermium (100), and mendelevium (101).

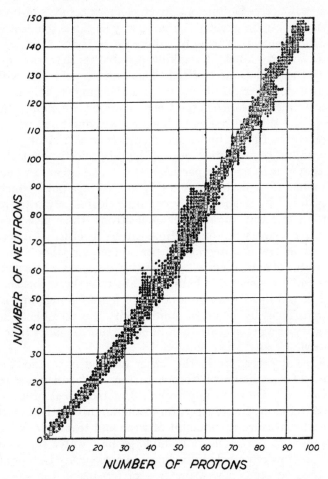

FIG. 13. *Chart of all known isotopes.*

The fact that every chemical element can be produced in a radioactive form has important implications not only for physics but for many other fields of science as well as for medicine, technology and industry. One of the many ways of using radioactive isotopes is the tracer method in which minute quantities of radioisotopes are employed. This is based on the fact that a radioactive isotope of a given element behaves chemically and biologically in exactly the same way as the stable isotope of the same element. The only difference is that the possession of radioactivity labels it, making possible its detection by observing the radiations emitted. This can be achieved with an extremely high sensitivity by using a counting technique.

The simplest of these is the Geiger counter, which in principle consists of a tube with a wire along its axis, and filled with a gas or a mixture of gases under specified pressure. A strong electric field is set up between the walls of the tube and the central wire, such that if a $\beta$- or an $\alpha$-particle entered the tube, it would set up a momentary discharge resulting in a voltage pulse which can be registered by means of any counting device, say a telephone meter. In this way the number of electrons which pass through the Geiger counter in a given time can be recorded. An activity as low as a few disintegrations per second, *i.e.* about one ten-thousandth of a microcurie, can be easily detected. For a medium weight radio-element of a half-life of about 10 days, this activity would be obtained from an amount of material weighing about $10^{-16}$ gm. Thus, by means of radioactivity it is possible to detect a quantity of a given material millions of times smaller than that detectable by any other method.

The usual procedure in the tracer method is to add a small amount of a radioactive isotope to the inert substance whose behaviour or history in any technical or biological process it is desired to follow. In industry, for example, this method has been applied to measure the amount of wear and tear of piston rings in engines, to detect leaks in underground water pipes, or to check the flow of petrol in pipelines. In agriculture isotopes have been used to study the utilization of fertilizers, the spread of plant diseases, or the uptake of various materials by plants. Finally, in medicine radioisotopes have found very wide applica-

Table III

SOME RADIOACTIVE ISOTOPES

| Isotope | Symbol | Half-Life | Radiation Emitted |
|---|---|---|---|
| Tritium | $^3T$ | 12·4 years | $e^-$ |
| Carbon-14 | $^{14}C$ | 5,568 years | $e^-$ |
| Sodium-24 | $^{24}Na$ | 15·06 hours | $e^-, \gamma$ |
| Phosphorus-32 | $^{32}P$ | 14.30 days | $e^-$ |
| Sulphur-35 | $^{35}S$ | 87·1 days | $e^-$ |
| Potassium-42 | $^{42}K$ | 12·44 hours | $e^-, \gamma$ |
| Calcium-45 | $^{45}Ca$ | 152 days | $e^-$ |
| Iron-59 | $^{59}Fe$ | 45·1 days | $e^-, \gamma$ |
| Cobalt-60 | $^{60}Co$ | 5·27 years | $e^-, \gamma$ |
| Zinc-65 | $^{65}Zn$ | 250 days | $e^+, \gamma$ |
| Bromine-82 | $^{82}Br$ | 35·87 hours | $e^-, \gamma$ |
| Iodine-131 | $^{131}I$ | 8·14 days | $e^-, \gamma$ |
| Caesium-137 | $^{137}Cs$ | 33 years | $e^-, \gamma$ |
| Thulium-170 | $^{170}Tm$ | 129 days | $e^-, \gamma$ |
| Tantalum-182 | $^{182}Ta$ | 111 days | $e^-, \gamma$ |
| Iridium-192 | $^{192}Ir$ | 74·37 days | $e^-, \gamma$ |
| Gold-198 | $^{198}Au$ | 2·69 days | $e^-, \gamma$ |

tions, both for the fundamental study of the processes going on in the living organism and as an aid in the diagnosis of disease. Another field of application utilizes the effects produced by the radiations themselves. In this case use is made of the fact that quantities of radioactivity exceeding hundreds of times those from the available natural radioactive elements can now be produced. In some cases radioactive isotopes having activities of thousands of curies can be easily manufactured. In fact, embarrassingly large quantities of radioisotopes become available as a by-product of atomic energy, and the problem is often how to dispose of it in a way which will not produce harm to living organisms.

Among the applications in which large quantities of radioisotopes are utilized are the detection of flaws in castings, sterilization of food products, and above all the treatment of cancer.

Not all radioisotopes can be used in these various applications. The half-life, the type of radiations emitted, the specific activity and availability have to be taken into account in the choice of radioactive isotopes. Table III gives a list of the radioisotopes most frequently employed.

It is said that the possibilities opened to research in technology and medicine by the availability of these artificially produced radioactive isotopes will in the end far exceed any gain which may result from the use of nuclear energy as a source of power. It has certainly already helped to make remarkable progress in a number of branches of science and industry, but the largest gains are still to come. The applications of radioactive isotopes may hold the key to the prosperity of future generations.

# CHAPTER III

## Smashing the atom

### The nucleus as a target

The discovery of radioactivity revealed for the first time the existence of enormous stores of energy within the atom. The energies of the particles emitted from radioactive substances are of the order of millions of electron-volts, as compared with a few electron-volts which is the energy released in atomic processes, such as chemical reactions. This discovery immediately raised the question whether it would be possible to make practical use of this huge store of energy. Apart, however, from this utilitarian motive, which is hardly ever given explicit recognition by scientists, there is the natural urge to find out all about the world around us, in this case, about the nucleus of the atom. Although much can be learned about the nucleus and its properties by the passive observation of the processes which nature displays for us in the phenomenon of radioactivity, it is clear that in order to gain a better insight into this subject a more active approach is needed. Furthermore, natural radioactivity is practically limited to heavy elements; of much greater value would be to know about the structure of light nuclei, since these are simple systems lending themselves more easily to theoretical analysis.

The question then is how to get at the nucleus. Apart from being extremely small it is also very inaccessible; it has a potential barrier around it which prevents the approach of other particles. The only way of getting to know about the nucleus seems to be by storm, by trying to break it up. The nucleus has often been likened to a little inaccessible island, surrounded by a high wall. The only possible way to find out something about the island and its inhabitants is to throw stones into it over the wall. By observing the directions in which the stones are hurled back one might make a guess about the intelligence of the inhabitants; if sometimes a different type of stone is thrown back it is possible to infer something about the mineral composition of the island. Similarly, in the case of the nucleus the only possible way to find out about its structure is to bombard it with some suitable projectile. In the days when Rutherford began his experiments the only suitable projectiles which had sufficient energy to penetrate the potential barrier were the a-particles emitted from radioactive substances. These were, therefore, the first to be used for the artificial disintegration of nuclei.

Before we discuss the results of such disintegrations we ought to make an attempt to calculate the chance of hitting a nucleus and producing a disintegration. First of all, we cannot aim at the target and we have to shoot at random. Secondly, the target is extremely small, the diameter of the nucleus being about ten thousand times smaller than the diameter of the atom. Thus, if a beam of a-particles is made to pass through matter, the chance of any one of them scoring a direct hit on the nucleus is very small indeed. If we consider the nucleus as a solid target the probability of hitting it would be proportional to the cross-section of the nucleus. Actually this probability depends on a number of other factors, such as the potential barrier around the nucleus, and the wave properties of the particles which may give rise to certain 'interference' effects and make the probability of hitting the nucleus either much smaller or much larger than the geometrical cross-section. Nevertheless, we still express this probability in terms of a cross-section. The unit for this cross-section is called a barn, which has a jocular origin 'as big as a barn'. One barn is an area of $10^{-24}$ cm.$^2$, which would be roughly the cross-sectional area of a particle of radius about $6 \times 10^{-13}$ cm. The relative areas of the nucleus and the atom are roughly the same as those of the *Queen Elizabeth* and the North Sea.

Small as the nuclear target may be, there are so many atoms in even a minute amount of material that if our projectile were allowed to proceed long enough it would be bound in the end to hit a nucleus. Unfortunately, the projectile, when it is a charged particle like the a-particle, is not allowed to proceed a long distance unmolested. As it penetrates through matter it interacts with a very large number of electrons of the atoms passed by.

Since electrons have a very small mass as compared with that of the a-particle, they may be thrown out from their atoms even when the a-particle passes at a relatively large distance from them. This process is called ionization. The amount of energy lost by an a-particle at each such ionization is very small—in air it is only about 32 electron-volts—but these ionizations are so numerous that the energy of the a-particle is very quickly used up. Thus, in passing through air at atmospheric pressure an a-particle may make about thirty thousand ionizing collisions along each centimetre of its path, losing in this way an energy of over 1 MeV. The energy of the a-particle is, therefore, very quickly dissipated and the particle is brought to rest before it has had a chance of making a collision with a nucleus. We see now why the range of an a-particle in air is only a few centimetres and why the track of an a-particle is straight (Plate VII); each of the ionizing events is far too feeble to deviate it from its course. It is only very rarely that an a-particle comes close enough to a nucleus to be deflected from its straight path, but occasionally this is observed. The track shown in the photograph of Plate VI shows such scattering events. This a-particle underwent two nuclear collisions: in one it was deflected only slightly from its course; in the other, near the end of its range, it suffered a much stronger deflection. In fact, it was the observation of the scattering of a-particles that led Rutherford to the concept of the atomic nucleus.

If, however, ordinary scattering is rare, the actual entry of an a-particle into the nucleus to cause its disintegration is a rarer event still. The reason for this is that even if an a-particle happens to score a direct hit on the nucleus it will not be able to enter into it unless it has a sufficient amount of energy. This is due to the existence of the potential barrier around the nucleus which was discussed in the previous chapter (Fig. 11). The graph of Fig. 11 shows the shape of the potential field as seen by an approaching charged particle. As the particle gets nearer to the nucleus the repulsive force acting between two positive charges increases, opposing its approach. The only way of overcoming it is to use a particle of an energy higher than that corresponding to the top of the potential barrier. The height of the barrier depends on the charge of the target and of the projectile; Fig. 14 shows the variation of the height of the barrier with the atomic number of the element for various projectiles. For α-particles and heavy nuclei it is about 25 MeV; in light nuclei it is much lower, for nitrogen it is of the order of about 5 MeV. As explained in the previous chapter, the projectile need not necessarily cross over the top of the barrier in order to enter the nucleus; its wave

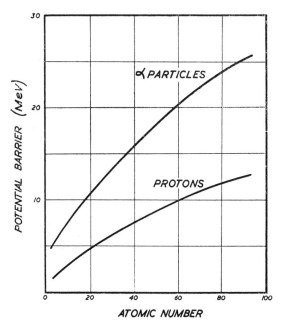

Fig. 14. *Potential barriers of nuclei.*

properties enable it to penetrate through the barrier. But the probability of such penetration decreases very rapidly with energy, and a particle of an energy considerably lower than the barrier height will have an extremely small chance of getting into the nucleus.

Summing up, there are two chief requisites for a successful nuclear disintegration: a very large number of projectiles, to ensure that a few will be left to score a hit before having dissipated their energy on ionization, and a high enough energy of the projectiles to overcome the potential barrier.

### The α-particle as a projectile

On the basis of these considerations the odds in favour of producing a disintegration by means of the α-particles from the radioactive substances appear quite low, for we are then restricted both in the number of the particles, as well as in their energy. Nevertheless, Rutherford carried out such an experiment in 1919 and was successful; he produced the first artificial nuclear disintegration. The target element was nitrogen which Rutherford bombarded with α-particles from Radium C. He found that as a result of this bombardment protons were emitted. In this experiment the α-particle source was put in a tube from which the air could be removed. At one end of the tube there was a metal foil sufficiently thick to stop the α-particles. On admitting nitrogen into the tube Rutherford observed the emission of particles through the foil, and these particles were identified as fast protons. The number of these protons was quite small, and it was calculated that only one α-particle in 100,000 succeeded in producing this reaction.

From the observation of the emission of protons Rutherford deduced that the following reaction had taken place:

$$^{14}N + {}^{4}He = {}^{17}O + {}^{1}H.$$

In other words, he postulated the transmutation of nitrogen and helium into oxygen and hydrogen.

This equation, written in the form of a chemical reaction, represents the first transmutation of elements performed by man. This was an event of such great importance that it is worth while to analyse it in greater detail. The reader may ask how we know that it was this and not some other reaction which took place. Since neither the oxygen nor the hydrogen are formed in sufficient quantity to be collected, how can one be sure about the products of this reaction?

The first thing to check about a nuclear reaction is that the total charge and the total number of particles remained unchanged, *i.e.* the number of protons and the number of neutrons must be the same on both sides of the equation. The symbol $^{14}N$ stands for 7 protons and 7 neutrons; therefore, the sum of particles on the left is 9 protons and 9 neutrons. $^{17}O$ has 8 protons and 9 neutrons; therefore, together with the emitted proton we have again 9 protons and 9 neutrons. This check by itself is, however, not sufficient, because we could write down several other equations which fulfil the same conditions. How do we know which reaction has taken place? This can be achieved by making use of two fundamental laws of classical physics, the laws of conservation of energy and of momentum. In any elastic collision, say between two billiards balls, the total energy and the total momentum before and after the collision must be the same. If one ball makes a head-on collision with another at rest, the first will come to a stop and the second will carry on in the forward direction with the energy and momentum previously had by the first particle. In off-centre collisions both balls will be set into motion at right angles to each other, and the direction and energy of each of the balls can be simply calculated from the conservation laws. Similarly, if an $\alpha$-particle collides with a helium nucleus both are set in motion at right angles to each other. We can often observe the paths of both particles after the collision in a cloud chamber and verify that the laws of conservation of energy and momentum hold for nuclear processes. Such a cloud chamber photograph is shown on Plate VIII. In this case the $\alpha$-particles were allowed to pass through a chamber filled with helium and a number of their tracks are seen. One of them is seen to fork producing two tracks at right angles to each other. By measuring the lengths of the three tracks in the fork we can determine the energies of the particles involved and their momenta. In this way it was possible to verify that the laws of conservation of energy and momentum hold strictly in nuclear collisions.

The same laws can be applied to the disintegration of nitrogen, but since this is not an elastic collision we have to consider the energy balance of the reaction. The target, the nitrogen nucleus, is initially at rest; the projectile, the $\alpha$-particle, has a known energy. But this is not the total energy involved. As was shown in the previous chapter, each nucleus has a certain binding energy;

the binding energies of the products of a nuclear reaction will on the whole be different from the binding energies of the initial nuclei. This means that in each nuclear reaction a certain amount of energy may be either released or absorbed, depending on whether the products are more or less stable than the original nuclei. This is taken into account by adding to the equation the so-called Q-value. The equation for the disintegration of nitrogen will, therefore, read:

$$^{14}N + {}^{4}He = {}^{17}O + {}^{1}H + Q.$$

The Q-value is a measure of the change in the binding energy resulting from the reaction. As has already been explained, the binding energy is obtained from the masses of the particles involved, and so the Q-value can be simply calculated from a knowledge of the atomic weights of all the isotopes involved. It is equal to the difference in the masses on both sides of the equation. Let us carry out the calculation. The atomic weights of nitrogen-14 and helium-4 are 14·007515 and 4·003873, giving a sum of 18·011388. The atomic weights of oxygen-17 and of hydrogen are 17·004533 and 1·008142, which adds up to 18·012675. We see that the sum on the left is smaller than the sum on the right, that is to say, we have produced particles heavier than the ones with which we started by 0·001287 units of atomic weight, which corresponds to an energy of 1·197 MeV. This, therefore, is the Q-value of the reaction. It is negative in this case, which means that this amount of energy has been lost in bringing the reaction about. This, of course, was to be expected when we remember that the $a$-particle is a very stable structure, and when it is broken up to take a proton from it, energy must be supplied. This energy has to come from the kinetic energy of motion of the $a$-particle which produces the reaction.

If this is taken into account, we know now how much energy is left over to be shared between the products $^{17}O$ and the proton. By applying the laws of conservation of momentum we can then calculate the proportion in which this energy is shared between the two products for any direction in which they may be emitted. Thus, in order to identify the reaction we have to measure the energies of the particles and the angles at which they are emitted in relation to the original direction of the α-particle and check whether they agree with the calculated values. This can again be done by means of the cloud chamber; the photograph of Plate IX shows an actual process of disintegration of nitrogen. We see there tracks of α-particles passing through a chamber filled with nitrogen. At one point a fork occurs in one of the tracks; the short track to the right is that of the oxygen nucleus formed, and the thin long track to the left of the emitted proton. From the ranges of these particles their energies can be determined; the angles are read off directly. It is found that the values thus obtained fit excellently with the calculated ones. This is a very sensitive test and can only be fulfilled for one type of reaction. Thus, although we are unable to see the particles themselves, such picture gives us as good evidence of this reaction having occurred as any directly obtained in an experiment.

Soon after Rutherford's experiment with nitrogen similar reactions were produced in many other elements. Some were of the same type, *i.e.* leading to the emission of protons, but other types of reaction were also observed; two of these, which have historical interest as being the first of their class, will be discussed now.

One of these is the emission of neutrons as a result of the bombardment of beryllium with α-particles. The formula of the reaction is

$$^{9}Be + {}^{4}He = {}^{12}C + {}^{1}n.$$

It was this reaction which led to the discovery of the neutron in 1932 by Chadwick, as described in Chapter I.

The Q-value of this reaction is $+5.71$ MeV, as can be verified by calculating the atomic weights of the particles involved given in Table II. In this case there is, therefore, a positive release of energy: most of it is taken up by the neutron which is, therefore, emitted with a large amount of energy. Although this reaction cannot be observed directly in the cloud chamber, since the neutron as a non-ionizing particle does not produce a cloud chamber track, it is possible sometimes to observe the track of the carbon-12 nucleus, and from this to deduce the direction and energy of the neutron. Once again the values are in complete agreement with those calculated on the basis of the laws of conservation of energy and momentum.

Neutrons themselves are best detected by making them collide with protons, *i.e.* by letting the neutron beam pass through a hydrogenous medium, say water or paraffin wax. Since the neutron and the proton have approximately the same mass their collision is analogous to that between two billiards balls. In a head-on collision the neutron is brought to rest and the proton is emitted in the forward direction with the whole energy. In off centre collisions the proton may be emitted at different angles but from the angle of emission and from the energy of the proton the energy of the neutron can be deduced.

The second type of reaction is that which led for the first time to the production of artificial radioactive isotopes. It was discovered by Irene Curie and Frederic Joliot who carried out experiments similar to Rutherford's but using aluminium as the target. They used a Geiger counter to detect the particles emitted, and noticed that the aluminium continued giving off radiations even after the bombarding projectiles, the $\alpha$-particles, were removed. They soon established that this radiation was of the $\beta$-type and that it was decaying gradually with a half-life of about three minutes. They interpreted this phenomenon as follows: as a result of the bombardment of aluminium with $\alpha$-particles, an isotope of phosphorus of mass number 30 and a neutron are produced according to the equation:

$$^{27}\text{Al} + {}^{4}\text{He} = {}^{30}\text{P} + {}^{1}\text{n}.$$

The product nucleus, phosphorus-30, is not an isotope found in nature. It contains 15 protons and 15 neutrons, but for so large a nucleus more neutrons than protons are needed to make it stable; this element is consequently unstable, and the transition to stability can be achieved by the transformation of one of its protons into a neutron, with the simultaneous emission of a positive electron. Thus, after the first reaction there follows the second reaction

$$^{30}\text{P} \rightarrow {}^{30}\text{Si} + \text{e}^{+}.$$

Immediately after this discovery was made in 1934 it was found that, far from being an exceptional event, such nuclear disintegrations in which unstable isotopes are produced occur very frequently.

*Artificial projectiles*

All disintegrations described so far were produced by using $\alpha$-particles as projectiles. It is clear, however, that these particles offer a rather limited scope for study. First, the number of projectiles is limited by the amount of radioactive substance available and this very seldom exceeded one gramme of radium. Taking into account that some nuclear reactions are produced at a rate of one for several million $\alpha$-particles, it is obvious that one needs a very intense source of radiation to study the reactions in detail. Even more important, however, is the fact that the energy of the $\alpha$-particles from the radioactive elements is strictly limited; the maximum energy is less than 9 MeV. This means that it is practically impossible to produce disintegrations in heavy nuclei, where the potential barrier is much higher, reaching 25 MeV (Fig. 14). On the other hand, the barrier for singly charged particles, *e.g.* protons, is much lower, and an energy of 12 million electron-volts would be sufficient to break up even a heavy nucleus. It seems, therefore, that a good case is made out for using projectiles made in the laboratory, if sufficiently intense beams of such particles could be produced. What is needed is a device in which charged particles would be accelerated to energies of the order of 10–20 million electron-volts. This was achieved in the various accelerators already referred to, of which there is now a very imposing array.

It started off in a very modest way with an energy of only 600,000 electron-volts. Although this energy is well below the potential barrier, even for light elements, it was thought that if a sufficiently large number of such low-energy projectiles were available, a small fraction of them might be able to penetrate this barrier and produce the disintegration. This was the idea in the minds of Cockcroft and Walton who built in 1932 a fairly simple high-voltage installation, using a transformer, rectifiers and condensers, to produce a potential of about 600,000 volts. By producing a beam of hydrogen ions and letting it pass through this potential difference they accelerated protons to an energy of 600,000 eV.

These protons were then used to bombard a lithium target.

The result was the emission from lithium of α-particles of very high energy, according to the reaction

$$^7\text{Li} + {}^1\text{H} = {}^4\text{He} + {}^4\text{He}.$$

If we put in the values of the atomic weights (Table II) we find that the Q-value is in this case 17·3 MeV. This large energy released in the reaction appears as the kinetic energy of the two α-particles, which are fired away in opposite directions. The tracks of these α-particles can easily be observed in a cloud chamber, and in this way the occurrence of this first nuclear disintegration produced entirely by artificial means could be confirmed.

This reaction is also important for the reason that it was the first to produce a large release of nuclear energy; we put in 0·6 MeV and obtain 17 MeV, nearly a thirtyfold gain. All the same it has no practical value as a source of energy, for the overall balance is strongly negative. This is so because the yield of this reaction is extremely small. At these low bombarding energies perhaps only one out of one hundred million protons would be able to penetrate the barrier to produce this reaction; all other protons lose their energy on ionization. The reason why we observe the reaction at all, despite its low yield, is that we start off with an enormous number of projectiles. The beam of protons produced in the accelerator constitutes an electric current which may be as much as several thousand microamperes, and even a current of one microampere corresponds to the emission of $6 \times 10^{12}$ protons per second, which is equivalent to nearly 200 grammes of radium. This illustrates the great advantage gained by using artificially produced projectiles. If this could be coupled with high energy as well, one might expect even more impressive results. This is the reason why immediately after Cockcroft's experiments there was such a rush to build accelerators giving intense beams of high-energy particles.

These particles are either protons which are obtained from hydrogen, or artificial α-particles which are obtained from helium. But the most effective of artificial projectiles turned out to be deuterons. The deuteron is the nucleus of deuterium (symbol D), an isotope of hydrogen of mass 2, and is composed of one proton and one neutron. The abundance of deuterium in nature is quite low, about one out of 7,000 hydrogen atoms is that of deuterium; nevertheless it is possible to separate it and obtain it in almost pure form. It is usually obtained as heavy water or deuterium oxide, which differs from ordinary water by the substitution of ordinary hydrogen by deuterium.

Deuterons have proved to be more effective projectiles than protons for the following reason. A deuteron passing near a nucleus may split up in flight; its neutron is captured by the nucleus and the proton flies on. Since a neutron has no charge there is no potential barrier for it and consequently such reaction can occur even with a projectile of a fairly low energy. Many of the nuclear reactions leading to the production of radioisotopes have been produced by means of the bombardment of various elements with deuterons.

Another frequent use of deuterons is as a source of neutrons. One of the best sources is the bombardment of deuterium with deuterons, according to the reaction

$$^2D + {}^2D = {}^3He + {}^1n.$$

*Particle accelerators*

One of the first accelerators to be developed was the electrostatic generator, or Van de Graaff machine, after the name of its inventor. It is a straightforward electrostatic machine in which a conductor is charged up to a high potential. Its principle is illustrated in Fig. 15. A spherical conductor is electrically insulated from the ground by means of a long cylinder of insulating material. A silk or rubber endless belt runs on pulleys from the bottom of the cylinder, which is at ground potential, to the top terminal. A positive electric charge is sprayed on to the belt which carries it to the upper conductor. In this way this conductor gradually receives a larger and larger charge and its potential goes up correspondingly. In principle it should be possible to raise the potential to any desired value but in practice there is a limit set by the breaking down of the insulation properties of the air, resulting either in a spark discharge or in a corona discharge on the surface of the conductor. These factors limit the potential obtainable to about 2 million volts. A higher potential can be achieved if the whole machine is enclosed in a tank filled with a gas at high pressure, preferably a gas in which discharges do not occur easily, such as nitrogen or 'Freon'. In this way, it is possible to increase considerably the final potential.

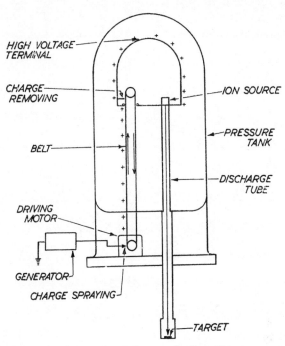

FIG. 15. *Principle of the van de Graaff generator.*

To produce the beam of projectiles a discharge tube is provided containing a hydrogen ion source at the top terminal. The protons or deuterons passing through the tube to the bottom are accelerated to the high energy. Several such generators, producing beams of particles of about 5 MeV, are in existence in various countries, and one of this type, built recently in the United States, delivers about 8 million volts. This seems to be about the limit obtainable in this type of generator. Although the Van de Graaff machine has many advantages, for it provides a fairly high current at a very well-defined and controllable energy, yet the limitation in energy makes it necessary to look for other accelerators.

One of the most successful accelerators in the field of nuclear disintegrations is the cyclotron invented by Lawrence in 1930. This is a machine in which particles are accelerated to high energies without actually using high potentials. The principle of the cyclotron is explained in Fig. 16. A copper box made up of

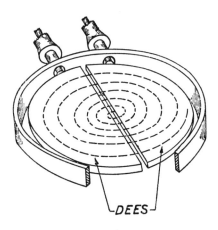

FIG. 16. *Principle of the cyclotron.*

two hollow semi-circular electrodes is situated between the poles of a powerful magnet. The two Dees, as they are called after their shape, are connected to a source of potential, say about 100,000 volts, alternating at a high frequency. An ion source in the centre of the box provides charged particles, say protons. The protons, being positively charged, will be accelerated towards one of the Dees which at that instant happens to be negatively charged. In crossing the gap they will thus gain an energy of 100,000 electron-volts. Since all this happens in a magnetic field the protons moving into the Dee will describe a semi-circular path and at a certain time afterwards will again reach the gap. By synchronizing the frequency of the voltage applied to the Dees with the time it takes for the particle to describe a semi-circle it can be so arranged that the protons will reach the gap just at the instant when the potential of the Dees has changed signs. The protons will, therefore, receive another acceleration from the same voltage, and having now a higher energy, 200,000 eV, will move in a circle of a larger radius. Although their path is now longer their velocity goes up in the same proportion and so it will take them the same time to reach the gap again; by that time the voltage will be reversed again and so the protons receive a further acceleration. This process is repeated many times; every time the protons pass the gap they receive an acceleration of 100,000 eV. The radius of their path gradually increases until they reach the end of the box. By that time they may have been accelerated about a hundred times so that their total energy will be 10 MeV. Thus by using a potential of only 100,000 volts, one obtains particles of an energy a hundred times greater.

Actually the final energy of the particles is independent of the voltage applied to the Dees, and is determined entirely by the radius of the magnet and the intensity of the magnetic field. Consequently, by increasing the size of the poles and the magnetic field, very high energies can be obtained. Plate XI shows a photograph of the cyclotron at Berkeley, California, which has a magnet with poles 60 inches in diameter, and in which deuterons can be accelerated to an energy of 24 MeV.

In this type of cyclotron there is a limit to the energy due to the increase of mass with velocity which follows from the theory of relativity (see Chapter VII). As the velocity of the particles increases so does their mass and consequently the time it takes to describe the circular path becomes longer, and the particles get out of phase. It has been found, however, that this difficulty can be overcome by varying the frequency of the voltage applied to the Dees. The cyclotron thus modified is known as the synchrocyclotron and it can be used to accelerate particles to very high energies. Several such machines with pole diameters up to 184 inches are now in existence, which produce beams of protons and a-particles up to 700 million electron-volts.

The reader may ask why we need to go to such high energies, of the order of 1,000 MeV, when about 30 MeV should be sufficient to climb over the highest potential barrier? There are several reasons for this. First, by using much higher energies we are able not just to chip off one or two particles from the nucleus but to break it into a large number of fragments. Such disintegration is called spallation and leads to many new types of unstable nuclei. Secondly, in order to study the nature of nuclear forces, which is associated with the emission and absorption of mesons, it is important to be able to produce these mesons artificially. For this purpose one needs particles of a sufficiently high energy. Some of these mesons have such a large mass that to produce them one needs more than 1,000 MeV, and this is the reason why there has been in recent years such a great drive to produce accelerators in which particles can be accelerated to energies of this order of magnitude. The general principle of these machines is somewhat similar to the synchrocyclotron, with the difference that both the high-frequency potential and the magnetic field vary. One starts off in these machines with particles which have already been accelerated to a few million electron-volts, by means of a Van de Graaff generator. This means that there is no need to use a solid magnet which would be prohibitively expensive, but a much cheaper magnet in the form of a ring. One such proton-synchrotron has recently been completed in Birmingham, where it produces protons of an energy of 1,000 MeV. Another such machine, at Brookhaven, is known as the cosmotron and has a ring magnet 30 feet in diameter. It produces protons of an energy of 3,000 million electron-volts. Plate XII shows a photograph of the cosmotron. The bevatron at Berkeley, a similar accelerator, produces protons of 6,000 MeV. Another machine of this type is being built at the European Organisation for Nuclear Research in Geneva, and it aims to produce particles of 25,000 million electron-volts.

### Neutrons as projectiles

We have so far not mentioned a projectile which does not require high energies, namely the neutron. The employment of neutrons to bombard nuclei has very great advantages. First of all, since a neutron does not ionize the atoms through which it passes, it does not lose any energy in passing through matter. It can only interact with a nucleus and consequently every neutron is bound eventually to produce a nuclear reaction. Secondly, as the neutron has no electrical charge it does not experience any repulsive force in approaching the nucleus. Fig. 17 shows the type of potential field around the nucleus as seen by a neutron. Instead of a barrier there is a flat potential until the neutron reaches the nucleus when it is immediately captured and falls into the well. Thus, one does not need neutrons of high energy in

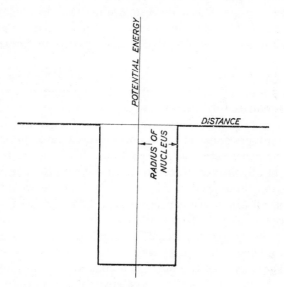

FIG. 17. *Potential field around a nucleus as seen by a neutron.*

order to produce nuclear reactions. In fact, slow neutrons are in this respect much more efficient than fast ones, simply because the lower the speed of the neutron the longer it remains within the sphere of influence of the nucleus and consequently the greater its chance of being captured by it. The slowing down of neutrons can be achieved easily by causing fast neutrons to collide with atoms of a light element, preferably with hydrogen. As already explained, at each collision with a proton the neutron loses a large fraction of its energy and so, after several collisions, the kinetic energy of the neutron is reduced to the energy of thermal agitation with which molecules of the substance move about in a given temperature. Such thermal neutrons, as they are called, have a very high probability of being captured; the cross-section for this process sometimes being of the order of several thousand barns, *i.e.* several thousand times higher than the actual geometrical cross-section of the nucleus. A very large number of disintegrations can thus be produced by neutrons and many radioactive isotopes have been manufactured in this way. A typical example of a 'capture' process is the production of radio-active sodium from ordinary sodium, according to the equation

$$^{23}Na + {}^1n = {}^{24}Na.$$

The energy released in this reaction (the binding energy of the neutron) is emitted in the form of $\gamma$-rays.

The reader may ask, if neutrons are so effective in producing nuclear disintegrations, why we bother about building the huge machines to accelerate charged particles. The answer to this is that, first of all, the reactions produced by charged particles are different from those produced by neutrons, and we are interested in studying all kinds of disintegrations; secondly, because there are no large sources of free neutrons available in nature. Very soon after a neutron is produced in a nuclear reaction it attaches itself to a nucleus met on its way and ceases to exist as a free particle. The only way to obtain neutrons has been by means of nuclear reactions, such as the bombardment of beryllium with $\alpha$-particles, or of deuterium with deuterons, in which neutrons are knocked out from nuclei. The problem was, therefore, brought back to disintegrations produced by charged particles.

The situation was radically changed early in 1939 when a new nuclear process was discovered which not only provided a new and extremely rich source of neutrons, but has transformed the whole field of nuclear physics from an academic subject into one carrying the most important practical implications. This process, nuclear fission, will be discussed in the next chapter.

# CHAPTER IV

## Energy from the atom

### Nuclear fission

The disintegration experiments described in the previous chapter, while of very great importance as the only means of providing information about the structure of the nucleus, are of no practical value, chiefly because of the small scale on which the nuclear reactions can be made to occur. Even with the most efficient cyclotron the number of nuclei that can be changed in an hour is of the order of $10^{15}$, while the number of atoms in one gram of a medium-weight substance is of the order of $10^{22}$. It is obvious that for the practical utilization of the energy of the nucleus one must either create conditions in which a considerable proportion of *all* nuclei of a substance are involved, or contrive a source of particles millions of times more intense than those produced in the accelerators. Such a source became available with the discovery of fission.

We know already that very heavy nuclei tend to be unstable because they contain many protons, and that if such a heavy nucleus should break up into two, a large amount of energy would be released, because the binding energy of medium-weight elements is much larger than of heavy ones. It turns out that such breaking up of a heavy nucleus, or fission as it is called, can be achieved by adding a neutron to the nucleus. The extra energy brought in by the neutron, which in the case of a slow neutron is its binding energy (about 8 MeV) is sufficient to disturb the delicately balanced equilibrium and to cause fission. The result of such fission is that a nucleus, like uranium, breaks up into two fragments of nearly equal weight. The fragments may be nuclei of krypton and barium, or of yttrium and iodine, or of any other two elements whose atomic numbers add up together to 92, the atomic number of uranium. It was in fact the chemical identification by Hahn and Strassmann of medium-weight elements produced as a result of the bombardment of uranium with neutrons, that led Frisch and Lise Meitner to interpret this discovery in terms of fission.

One of the chief features of fission is the large release of energy. This follows from the difference in binding energies per nucleon for heavy and medium elements. From the graph of Fig. 10 it is seen that this difference is about 0·9 MeV (million electron-volt) per nucleon. Since the uranium has nearly 240 nucleons, the total energy released is about 200 MeV. This energy appears initially mainly as the kinetic energy of the two fragments; owing, however, to their very intense ionization the energy is soon dissipated and converted into heat.

The next feature is that both fragments are radioactive. This, too, is to be expected when we recall that in heavy nuclei the ratio of neutrons to protons is greater than in medium nuclei. The fission fragments have, therefore, too many neutrons, and this can be adjusted in the usual way, by a transformation of a neutron into a proton with the emission of a $\beta$-ray. In fact, the neutron surplus is so great that, in general, the new nucleus undergoes again a similar decay, and so we have not two but a series of several radioactive isotopes following each other. Altogether, over 200 radioactive isotopes covering 34 elements, from zinc to europium, have been identified as fission fragments.

The most important feature, however, is the emission of several fast neutrons at fission. This, too, is a result of the large surplus of neutrons at the breaking up of the heavy nucleus. In the case of uranium the average number of neutrons emitted at each fission is 2·5, and these few neutrons make all the difference, because they open the way for a self-sustained nuclear chain reaction. Each neutron emitted at fission can be made to hit another uranium nucleus, causing further fission, which emits more neutrons, and so on. If, for the sake of argument, we assume that 2 neutrons are available to produce further fission then if we start with 1 neutron we shall have 2 neutrons in the first generation, 4 neutrons in the next, over 1 million after 20 generations, $10^{12}$ after 40 generations, $10^{18}$ after 60 generations, and $10^{24}$ neutrons after 80 generations. Thus, we see that we need only to allow the

PLATE I. The 'Horsehead' nebula in Orion, south of Zeta Orionis, in red light. A galactic nebula.

(*200-inch Hale reflector. By courtesy of the Mount Wilson and Palomar Observatories.*)

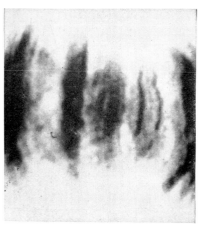
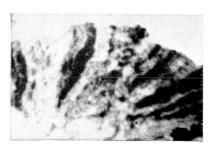

PLATE II. Sections of chromosomes.

Left: As photographed with the ultra-violet microscope.
Right: As photographed with the electron microscope.

*(From 'The sub-microscopic structure of the Balbiano-Ring.' by W. Beermann and G. F. Bahr, Experimental Cell Research 6, 195-201, 1954, by courtesy of the authors.)*

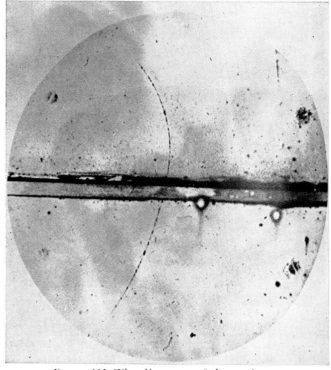

PLATE III. The discovery of the positron.
*(From The Physical Review. By courtesy of the American Institute of Physics.)*

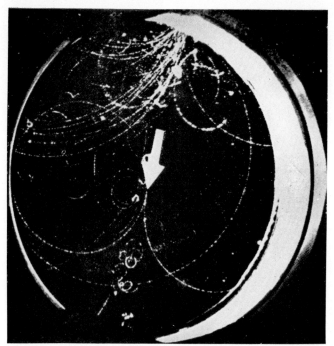

PLATE IV. Pair-production.
*(By courtesy of Prof. P. G. Kruger.)*

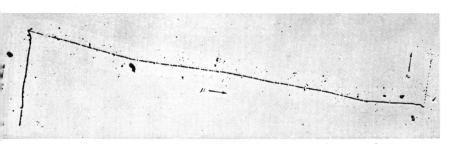

PLATE V. Transformation of a π-meson into a μ-meson into an electron.
*(By courtesy of Prof. C. F. Powell.)*

PLATE VI. Track of α-particle showing nuclear scattering.
*lates VI, VII and VIII are taken from* Radiations from Radioactive Substances by Rutherford, Chadwick and Ellis, *by courtesy of the Cambridge University Press.)*

PLATE VII. Tracks of α-particles from Thorium C and C′.

PLATE VIII. Scattering of α-particles by helium.

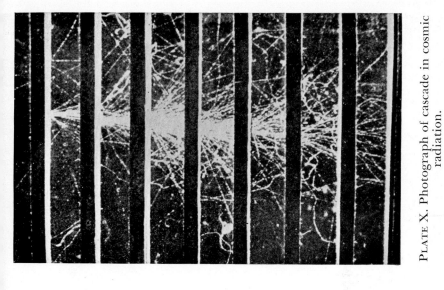

PLATE X. Photograph of cascade in cosmic radiation.

PLATE IX. Disintegration of nitrogen by α-particles.

(*By courtesy of Prof. P. M. S. Blackett.*)

PLATE XI. 60-inch cyclotron at Berkeley.
*(By courtesy of the University of California Radiation Laboratory.)*

PLATE XII. Cosmotron at Brookhaven.
*(By courtesy of Brookhaven National Laboratory.)*

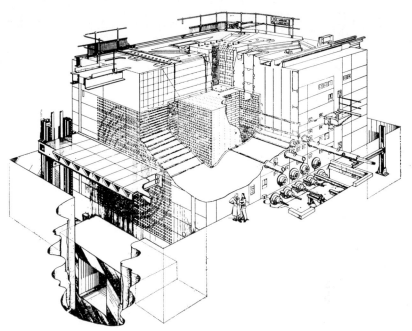

PLATE XIII. Diagram of BEPO (nuclear reactor at Harwell).

PLATE XIV. Photograph of exterior of BEPO.

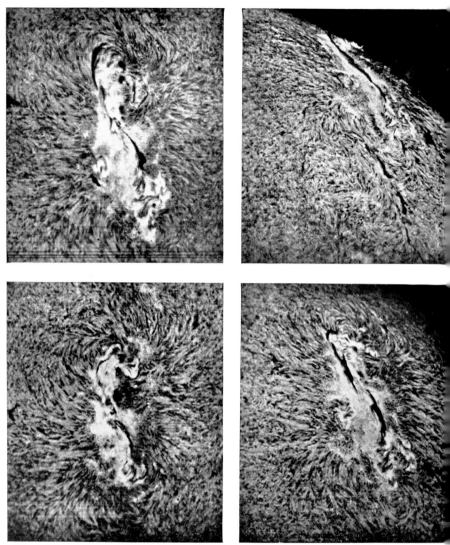

PLATE XV. Four photographs of the S.W. quarter of the sun taken
with the red hydrogen line (Hα) on August 3rd, 5th, 7th and 9th, 1915.

(By courtesy of the Mount Wilson and Palomar Observatories.)

PLATE XVI. Jupiter, in red light. Satellite Ganymede and
shadow (above).

*(200-inch Hale reflector. By courtesy of the Mount Wilson and Palomar
Observatories.)*

PLATE XVII. Saturn, in blue light.

*(200-inch Hale reflector. By courtesy of the Mount Wilson and Palomar
Observatories.)*

BLUE

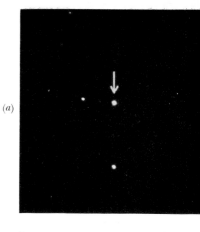

(*a*)

RED

PLATE XVIII. Mars, in blue and red light.
(*200-inch Hale reflector. By courtesy of the Mount Wilson and Palomar Observatories.*)

PLATE XIX (*right*). Supernova in the extragalactic nebula IC 4182. Three views: 1937, 1938 and 1942.

(*a*) 1937, Sept. 10th. Exposure 20 m. Maximum brightness.

(*b*) 1938, Nov. 24th. Exposure 45 m. Faint.

(*c*) 1942, Jan. 19th. Exposure 85 m. Too faint to observe.

(*100-inch Hooker reflector. By courtesy of the Mount Wilson and Palomar Observatories.*)

(*b*)

(*c*)

PLATE XX. The Crab nebula, in red light. A galactic nebula.
*(200-inch Hale reflector. By courtesy of the Mount Wilson and Palomar Observatories.)*

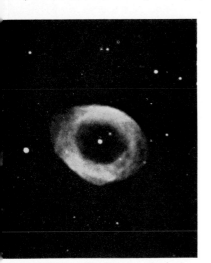

PLATE XXI. The Ring nebula in
Lyra. A galactic nebula.

*. S. Plaskett. By courtesy of the Director of*
*Dominion Astrophysical Observatory, Royal*
*Oak, B.C., Canada.)*

PLATE XXII. The surface structure
of a metal.

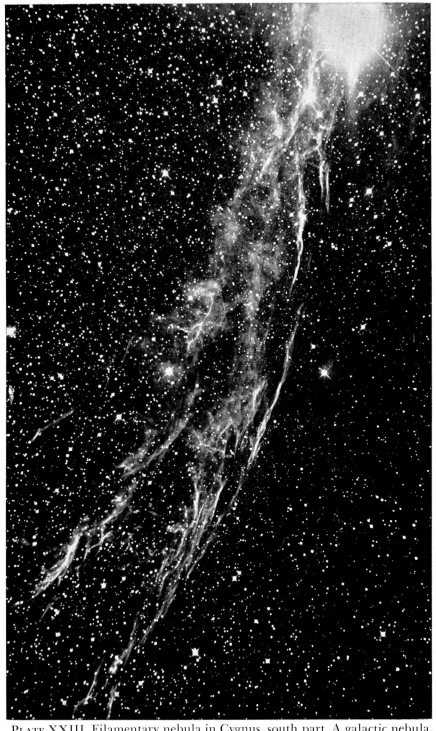

PLATE XXIII. Filamentary nebula in Cygnus, south part. A galactic nebula.
(60-*inch reflector. By courtesy of the Mount Wilson and Palomar Observatories.*)

PLATE XXIV. Great nebula in Orion, Messier 42. A galactic nebula.
(100-*inch Hooker reflector. By courtesy of the Mount Wilson and Palomar Observatories.*)

PLATE XXV. Globular star-cluster, Messier 3.

*(200-inch Hale reflector. By courtesy of the Mount Wilson and Palomar Observatories.)*

PLATE XXVI. The Whirlpool nebula, Messier 51.

*(Ritchie. By courtesy of the Mount Wilson and Palomar Observatories.)*

PLATE XXVII. Great spiral in Andromeda, Messier 31.
*(48-inch Schmidt telescope. By courtesy of the Mount Wilson and Palomar Observatories.)*

PLATE XXVIII. Spiral nebula in Virgo, seen edge on, Messier 104.
*(200-inch Hale reflector. By courtesy of the Mount Wilson and Palomar Observatories.)*

PLATE XXIX. Unresolved elliptical nebula, NGC 3115.

(*60-inch reflector. By courtesy of the Mount Wilson and Palomar Observatories.*)

PLATE XXX. Elliptical nebula, NGC 147, in Andromeda, showing resolution into stars, in red light.

(*200-inch Hale reflector. By courtesy of the Mount Wilson and Palomar Observatories.*)

| CLUSTER NEBULA IN | DISTANCE IN LIGHT-YEARS | RED-SHIFTS |
|---|---|---|

H+K

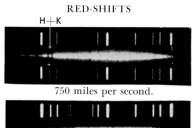

| | | |
|---|---|---|
| Virgo. | 7,500,000 | 750 miles per second. |
| Ursa Major. | 100,000,000 | 9,300 miles per second. |
| Corona Borealis. | 130,000,000 | 13,400 miles per second. |
| Bootes. | 230,000,000 | 24,400 miles per second. |
| Hydra. | 350,000,000 | 38,000 miles per second. |

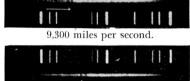

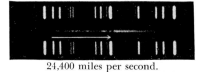

Red-shifts are expressed as velocities, $c \, d\lambda/\lambda$. Arrows indicate shift for calcium lines H and K. One light-year equals about 6 trillion miles, or $6 \times 10^{12}$ miles.

PLATE XXXI. Relation between red-shift and distance for extra-galactic nebulae. Distances uncorrected for new scale factor.

(*By courtesy of the Mount Wilson and Palomar Observatories.*)

chain reaction to proceed long enough to produce any number of neutrons.

Two conditions must be fulfilled to make such a chain reaction possible. First, we must ensure that the neutrons are not captured by nuclei in a way which does not lead to fission. This means that we must have an assembly of pure fissile material without significant quantities of substances which absorb neutrons. Secondly, we must ensure that the neutrons will not be able to escape from the assembly before producing further fission. Since we know how far a neutron will travel between two collisions, we can calculate the minimum amount of material which is required to maintain a chain reaction. This minimum amount is called the critical mass. It is impossible to set up a divergent chain reaction unless an amount of material greater than the critical mass is assembled.

On the other hand, once such an amount is assembled a chain reaction, with a possible catastrophic result, will take place immediately, since the time between two successive fissions is about $10^{-8}$ seconds, and so an enormous release of energy may occur in an extremely short time. This raises the question of how to control the reaction.

The chief way to keep the chain reaction under control is by introducing into the fissile material a substance which absorbs neutrons. Depending on how much of this substance is put in, the number of neutrons available for further fission can be made either smaller or greater than one. Only in the latter case would a divergent chain reaction develop. If, therefore, we start off with a large amount of the absorber in the uranium and then gradually withdraw it we can build up the neutron population in it to the desired value. If we then put some absorber back, so that after each fission exactly one neutron is available to produce further fission, the reaction will proceed from then onwards at a steady rate, with the total number of neutrons, and consequently the power produced, remaining constant.

The gradual build-up of the chain reaction is made possible by the fact that not all neutrons are emitted instantaneously upon fission. A small fraction of them, of the order of 1 per cent, are emitted with some delay, ranging from a few seconds to a few minutes after the fission, and it is these delayed neutrons which make the control so easy and safe. If we approach the critical condition slowly, so as not to have too large an excess of neutrons, the maintenance of the chain reaction is dependent on the delayed neutrons, because the prompt neutrons by themselves would not be sufficient to make a divergent reaction. The multiplication of neutrons will, therefore, proceed slowly with the period of the delayed neutrons, giving plenty of time to make adjustments. In fact, the multiplication time of the reaction can be made as long as several hours. The power level can thus be controlled very easily and the danger of an explosion is practically eliminated.

*Nuclear reactors*

An arrangement in which a chain reaction based on fission can be established and its power level controlled is called a nuclear reactor. There are various types of nuclear reactors, differing in the kind of fissile material they employ, the energy of the neutrons, the temperature at which they run, and above all in their purpose, *e.g.* whether they are built for the production of power or to make use of the high neutron flux in the reactor.

The choice of fissile material often determines the construction of the reactor. Natural uranium contains mainly the isotope $^{238}U$; only 1 atom in 140 belongs to the lighter isotope $^{235}U$. These two isotopes have quite different fission properties. Uranium-238 requires more than the neutron binding energy to break it up, and consequently only neutrons which have a kinetic energy above 1 million electron-volts are capable of producing fission. The neutrons emitted at fission have a wide distribution of energies, and many are below 1 MeV; this means that only a fraction of them can be utilized for further fission. Moreover, uranium-238 has a fairly high probability of absorbing neutrons without producing fission, a process which will be discussed in more detail later on. The result of these two effects is that it is impossible to maintain a chain reaction in uranium-238, no matter how much of the material is assembled.

On the other hand, uranium-235 has been found to undergo fission with neutrons of all energies. In fact, thermal neutrons have a very high probability of producing fission. Furthermore, this isotope does not absorb neutrons appreciably. Consequently, it is very easy to set up a chain reaction in uranium-235, and the critical size is very small, probably of the order of one kilogramme. Since, however, uranium-235 is present in natural uranium in a very low proportion, it has to be separated from the bulk by means of one of the very laborious and costly techniques of isotope separation.

In natural uranium it is impossible to maintain a chain reaction with fast neutrons, since such neutrons have only a small probability of producing fission in uranium-235. On the other hand, it is possible to achieve this with slow neutrons. Since the neutrons emitted at fission are fast ones, they have to be slowed down before they hit other uranium nuclei. This slowing-down process is called moderation and can be achieved by making the neutrons collide with atoms of light elements. The best element would be hydrogen, but it also absorbs neutrons, and the combined loss of neutrons by hydrogen and uranium-238 is so great that the reaction is inhibited. For this reason other moderators have to be found.

The moderator most widely used is graphite, since carbon absorbs neutrons to a very small extent. The so-called carbon pile is an arrangement consisting of an assembly of graphite bricks in which uranium rods are inserted at intervals, forming a lattice. The neutrons emitted from the uranium pass through the graphite, where they are slowed down, and as such have a much higher probability of causing fission in the uranium rods. Owing to the low proportion of the fissile material and to the relative inefficiency of carbon as a moderator the critical size is much greater, and may be of the order of 10 tons or more of natural uranium. Plate XIII shows a diagram of BEPO, the nuclear reactor at Harwell, which contains 40 tons of uranium, and can develop power of 6,000 kW. Plate XIV shows a photograph of the exterior of BEPO; one can see on it mainly the very heavy concrete walls surrounding the pile; these are necessary to provide shielding from the intense neutron and $\gamma$-radiation issuing from the reactor.

Although uranium-235 is the only naturally occurring fissile material in which a chain reaction can be set up, there are several other artificially produced materials which can serve the same purpose. One of these is plutonium-239, an isotope of atomic number 94, which is obtained from uranium-238 as a result of the latter capturing a neutron. Uranium-238 is then transformed into uranium-239, which is a radioactive element and decays by the emission of a $\beta$-ray into neptunium-239. This too is radio-active, and after another $\beta$-emission is transformed into plutonium-239.

Since plutonium does not exist in nature it has to be produced, atom by atom, by means of this process. To carry this out on a practical scale one would need an enormous number of neutrons, which can only be provided in a nuclear reactor. In fact, the first nuclear reactors, which were based on natural uranium, were built for the sole purpose of manufacturing plutonium. Once having produced a sufficient amount of plutonium this can then be used by itself as a fissile material in the same way as uranium-235.

Another possibility is to utilize thorium. If thorium-232 is bombarded with neutrons it is converted into the isotope thorium-233, which decays into protactinium-233, and this in turn into uranium-233. Uranium-233 is a fissile material with properties similar to those of uranium-235 or plutonium-239.

### The atom bomb

In the discussion of nuclear reactors emphasis was laid on the conditions which ensure steady operation of the reactor, so that the power output will be constant and the reaction will never get out of hand. Quite opposite are the requirements for a weapon. In this case it is desired to release a large amount of energy in the shortest possible time. It is obvious that fast neutrons must be used for this purpose, because the slowing-down time of a neutron is of the order of $10^{-4}$ seconds, which means that it may take about one hundredth of a second to produce some 80 generations of neutrons. This is far too long a time to make an effective weapon. With fast neutrons, however, 80 generations of neutrons could be developed in less than a millionth of a second. This is the reason why an atom bomb needs either pure uranium-235 or plutonium-239, and it was for this purpose that the first nuclear reactors as well as the big isotope separation plants were developed during the war.

The mechanism of the atom bomb has never been revealed, although its principle is quite simple. One would have to start with two pieces of fissile material, each smaller than the critical size, and at the desired moment bring them together quickly. The emphasis is on quick assembly, as otherwise the heat developed in the earlier fissions may disperse the system before a large number of fissions had time to build up. A rapid assembly may be achieved by shooting the two parts of fissile material together by means of ordinary explosives. If, say, $10^{24}$ fissions are developed, the heat produced will be $10^{13}$ calories and the explosive power equivalent to 20,000 tons of T.N.T. This was said to be the explosive power of the first atom bomb dropped over Hiroshima in 1945. Later modifications have made it possible to use a larger number of fragments, by an implosion mechanism, and to increase the explosive power of the bomb about 25 times.

*Thermonuclear reactions*

The fission process has made possible for the first time the release of the energy in the nucleus on a practical scale. There is, however, yet another way in which this could be achieved. From the binding energy curve (Fig. 10) it is clear that energy would be released at the fusion of light elements into heavier ones. In particular, we have found that helium is a very stable nucleus; if, therefore, hydrogen could be converted into helium, a large amount of energy would be released.

The previous discussions have indicated the difficulties which would be encountered in attempting to produce large-scale nuclear disintegrations by means of charged particles. First, the majority of such particles would lose their energy on ionizing the atoms through which they pass. Secondly, the particles would have to possess a sufficiently high energy to penetrate the potential barrier of the nucleus, and we have seen that it would be impossible to produce a really large number of such projectiles. At first sight, therefore, it would appear that the maintenance of a nuclear reaction by means of charged particles is impossible on a large scale. The situation is, however, quite different if we consider a system at a very high temperature. At a temperature of the order of many millions of degrees, the atoms are stripped of their electrons, and all matter consists of a mixture of bare nuclei and free electrons moving about with the speed of thermal agitation. There is, therefore, no loss of energy at collision with electrons, and the nuclei have a good chance to collide with each other. If the temperature were so high that the nuclei had an

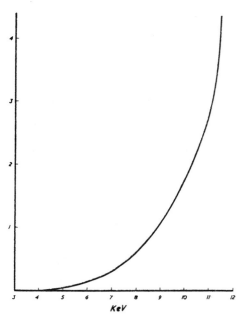

Fig. 18. *Excitation function at low energies.*

energy greater than the potential barrier, every such collision would give rise to a disintegration. We know, however, that the energy of a projectile need not be as great as the potential barrier in order to produce a disintegration. The wave properties of the particle enable it to penetrate through the potential wall even if its energy is quite low. Indeed, it has been found that protons of an energy as low as a few thousand electron-volts can produce disintegrations in light elements. Naturally, the lower the energy the smaller the probability of penetrating the barrier. Fig. 18 shows a typical excitation function, or probability of producing a disintegration as a function of the energy of the bombarding particle. It is seen how very rapidly the probability goes up with an increase in energy. If, however, we have a large number of projectiles which do not lose energy in any other way, and if we can afford to wait long enough, then nuclear disintegrations are bound to take place even at low energies.

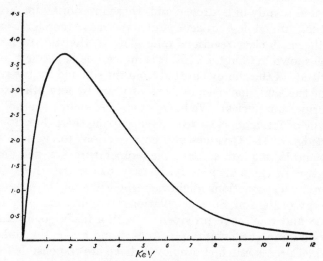

FIG. 19. *Distribution of energies of particles at a temperature of* 20 *million degrees C.*

These considerations show that it should be possible to produce large-scale nuclear disintegrations if a substance is heated to a temperature at which the particles have an energy of a few thousand electron-volts. An energy of about 10,000 eV (10 KeV) corresponds to a temperature of 100 million degrees Centigrade, but a somewhat lower temperature would still do. This is so because at a given temperature not all particles move with the same energy. If we were to measure the energy of individual particles at a given temperature we should find a very wide distribution, of the type shown on Fig. 19. This distribution of energies is for a temperature of about 20 million degrees Centigrade. It is seen that while the *average* energy of the particles at this temperature is about 2 KeV, there are many particles which have an energy between 5 and 10 KeV. Thus, we conclude that if hydrogen could be heated to a temperature of about 20 million degrees a large-scale thermonuclear reaction would take place.

*Nuclear reactions in the sun and stars*

The conditions just described are fulfilled in the sun, which is composed mainly of hydrogen and whose interior temperature is about 20 million degrees centigrade. We may, therefore, expect that thermonuclear reactions take place in the sun. In fact, as will be shown in Chapter VIII, it is impossible to account for the magnitude of the energy emitted from the sun and for the steady rate of this emission over millions of years by any other source of energy than nuclear. We have, of course, no direct proof as to the type of thermonuclear reaction occurring there, but from our knowledge of the Q-values and cross-sections for various reactions, and taking into account the temperature, size and density of matter in the sun, it is fairly easy to deduce which of the known nuclear reactions might be responsible for the production of energy in the sun. Such calculations were first made by Bethe in 1938 and they have provided us with a fairly good basis for understanding the nuclear processes going on in the sun. The two chief processes which we now believe are responsible for the sun's energy are the hydrogen chain and the carbon cycle.

The hydrogen chain is represented by the following formulae:

$$^1H + {}^1H = {}^2D + e^+,$$
$$^2D + {}^1H = {}^3He,$$
$$^3He + {}^3He = {}^4He + {}^1H + {}^1H.$$

We start off with two protons colliding with each other. An assembly of two protons is, of course, unstable, owing to the electrostatic repulsion between them, but it may become a stable structure if one of the protons changes into a neutron with the emission of a positron. Thus, the result of this encounter is the production of a nucleus of hydrogen containing one proton and one neutron, in other words, a deuteron, the nucleus of heavy hydrogen. In the next stage, another proton collides with the deuteron to produce the nucleus of helium 3, containing 2 protons and 1 neutron. In the final stage two such helium nuclei, formed in two different collisions, meet each other. They combine to form a nucleus of helium 4, and 2 protons. The final balance, therefore, is that we have put into the reaction 6 protons and obtained an $\alpha$-particle and 2 protons. Effectively, therefore, it is a fusion of 4 protons into an $\alpha$-particle, with the production of 2 positrons. We know already that the $\alpha$-particle is a very stable structure and that its binding energy is about 28 MeV.

The other process, which is called the carbon cycle, takes place in four stages, which are represented in the following formulae:

$$^{12}C + {^1}H = {^{13}}N \rightarrow {^{13}}C + e^+,$$
$$^{13}C + {^1}H = {^{14}}N,$$
$$^{14}N + {^1}H = {^{15}}O \rightarrow {^{15}}N + e^+,$$
$$^{15}N + {^1}H = {^{12}}C + {^4}He.$$

In the first stage a proton hits a carbon nucleus. The result of this reaction is the formation of a nucleus of nitrogen-13 containing 7 protons and 6 neutrons. This nucleus, however, is unstable, as it contains too many protons, and consequently one of the protons changes into a neutron, with the emission of a positron, resulting in the formation of a nucleus of carbon-13, which has 6 protons and 7 neutrons. In the next stage this carbon nucleus is hit by another proton, which combines with it to form the nucleus of nitrogen-14 containing 7 protons and 7 neutrons.

In the third stage this nitrogen nucleus is hit by a third proton. The nucleus formed, oxygen-15, contains 8 protons and 7 neutrons and is again unstable, having too many protons. One of the protons changes into a neutron with the emission of a positron, resulting in the formation of nitrogen-15. Finally, in the last stage, a fourth proton hits this newly formed nucleus nitrogen-15, breaking it up into the nuclei of carbon-12 and helium. Thus we have got back the carbon nucleus with which we started the reaction. This means that carbon itself is not being used up in this process but only acts as a catalyst. The final balance is that we have put in 4 protons and obtained 1 α-particle and 2 positrons.

We see, therefore, that in both these processes, the hydrogen chain and the carbon cycle, we deal ultimately with the same reaction, with the fusion of hydrogen into helium, with the simultaneous emission of energy. Which of these processes takes place predominantly depends on various other conditions, particularly on the size of the star. It is nowadays believed that in the sun the hydrogen chain is the predominant reaction, while in larger stars the carbon cycle is the chief source of energy.

At the temperature of the sun both the hydrogen chain and the carbon cycle are very slow processes. Apart from the fact that several stages of the reaction involve radioactive transformations which are slow in time, the main delay is due to the small probability of penetrating the barrier at collision. Thus, the period of time for the whole carbon cycle to take place is calculated to be about six million years.

The reason why most of the energy in the stars comes from the burning of hydrogen is because hydrogen is the main constituent of stars; and since it requires the lowest temperature for a thermonuclear reaction, only hydrogen fusion takes place. Should, however, the supply of hydrogen be exhausted, then other elements, in the first place helium, may take over to produce thermonuclear reactions. The exhaustion of hydrogen would cause the star to contract through gravitation and thus increase its temperature until about 100 million degrees, when thermonuclear reactions in helium may occur. As a result of burning of helium, carbon may be produced, and after helium has been exhausted a further contraction may raise the temperature still further, to about 600 million degrees, when carbon may be ignited, and so on. There is reason to believe that some stars have already reached those stages, but the majority of stars still burn hydrogen as this is the most abundant element in the universe.

*The hydrogen bomb*

The possibility of setting up a thermonuclear reaction on the earth was considered unrealistic until 1945, since the highest temperatures which could at that time be achieved in the laboratory were much less than 100,000 degrees centigrade, while for thermonuclear reactions a temperature of the order of millions of degrees is necessary. The situation changed, however, after the development of the atom bomb based on fission. At the instant of the explosion the temperature reaches several million degrees, and although this lasts only an extremely short time it may be sufficient to initiate a fusion reaction. By its very nature such a reaction could only be utilized as an explosive, and such an arrangement is known as the hydrogen bomb.

Despite its name it is clear that ordinary hydrogen cannot be used as an explosive. We have already seen that the solar reactions, the hydrogen chain and the carbon cycle, are very slow. Any process which depends on a $\beta$-decay, the transformation of a proton into a neutron, is far too slow to be suitable for a thermonuclear explosion. There are, however, isotopes of hydrogen which appear to be more suitable for thermonuclear reactions. One is the so-called d-d reaction in which two deuterons are made to collide. The formula is

$$^2D + {}^2D = {}^3He + {}^1n,$$

and the Q-value for this process is 3·3 MeV. This reaction has already been mentioned (Chapter III) as a source of neutrons.

The other reaction, the d-t process, is based on a third isotope of hydrogen, called tritium (symbol T), the nucleus of which, the triton, consists of 1 proton and 2 neutrons. When a deuteron and a triton meet, they are converted into an $\alpha$-particle and a neutron according to the formula

$$^3T + {}^2D = {}^4He + {}^1n,$$

with a Q-value of 17·6 MeV.

Because of its higher Q-value the tritium reaction will produce much more heat for a given number of collisions than the d-d process. Much more important, however, is the fact that at a given temperature the tritium reaction will proceed much faster than the deuterium one. Fig. 20 shows the heat output from each of these reactions as a function of temperature. It is of interest to note first how very sensitive the output of thermonuclear reactions is to temperature; the vertical scale is a logarithmic one, while the horizontal is a linear scale. It is seen that doubling the temperature, say increasing it from 1 to 2 million degrees, increases the energy output by a factor of nearly a million. The comparison of the two curves shows that at a given temperature the tritium reaction yields several hundred times more heat per gramme of substance burned than the deuterium reaction. It is believed that the short time during which the necessary high temperature is maintained in the atom bomb is not sufficient to

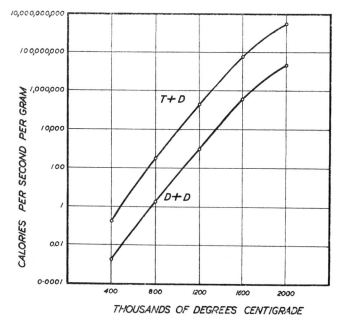

FIG. 20. *Output of heat from some thermonuclear reactions.*

start a reaction in deuterium alone, and that consequently a mixture of tritium with deuterium is necessary. If this were true, a hydrogen bomb would be prohibitively expensive owing to the high cost of tritium. This isotope does not exist in nature, and can be obtained only through a nuclear reaction. The best process seems to be the bombardment of lithium with neutrons according to the formula

$$^6Li + {}^1n = {}^4He + {}^3T.$$

To make tritium on a large scale one would have to put the lithium into a nuclear reactor where it would be bombarded with neutrons. This process of manufacture of tritium is, therefore, somewhat similar to that of making plutonium, except that one would need 80 times more neutrons to make tritium than to make the same weight of plutonium. Moreover, while plutonium has a very long half-life (about 24,000 years) the half-life of tritium is only 12·4 years, and so it would be very wasteful to store the tritium.

Apart from the high cost of tritium, the deuterium and tritium would have to be used in liquid form in order to obtain a sufficiently high density. The need of a liquefying system would make such a 'device' very heavy and bulky.

It is believed that a solution to this difficulty was found by making tritium on the spot, at the instant of the explosion, instead of in a nuclear reactor. For this purpose a compound lithium-6 deuteride ($^6$LiD) is employed. If this substance is put round an atom bomb assembly, then at the instant of the explosion the neutrons emitted at fission bombard lithium-6 producing tritium. At the high temperature of the explosion the tritium combines with the deuterium to start a thermonuclear reaction.

Several such hydrogen bombs have been exploded for test purposes, and in one of them an explosive power of 17 million tons of T.N.T., or nearly 1,000 times greater than the Hiroshima bomb, has been achieved. It is believed, however, that most of the explosive power came in this case not from the thermonuclear reaction but from fission induced by fast neutrons in an outer shell of uranium-238. The thermonuclear reaction served in that case mainly as a source of fast neutrons.

Although thermonuclear reactions have so far been used only for military purposes, it is conceivable that an arrangement may be found for their utilization as a source of power. For example, by means of a very intense electric discharge it may be possible to produce high-temperature 'pulses' which will give rise to thermonuclear reactions in bursts. If one may judge from the rate of progress in nuclear physics in recent years, such speculations may soon become reality.

# CHAPTER V

# Cosmic radiation

## The composition of cosmic rays

Cosmic radiation is one of the most fascinating subjects in physics. Many aspects of it appeal to the adventurous spirit in the scientist. Its study involves going down into caves or deep under water, climbing high mountains or sending up balloons to reach the upper regions of the atmosphere. All these activities, which call forth not only the purely scientific but also the exploring urge in man, have probably contributed to the great popularity of this subject, particularly among young physicists. Its importance for nuclear physics derives from the fact that in cosmic radiation we find particles of energy millions of times greater than it has so far been possible to achieve artificially, even in the largest accelerators. It is from the study of particles of very high energy that we can hope to solve the problem of the elementary particles and the ultimate structure of matter.

Very soon after the discovery of radioactivity, it was observed that a small but definite ionizing current could be observed even in the absence of any radioactive source. We now know that at ground level over land much of this current is due to radioactive contamination, *i.e.* to radon present in the atmosphere and to small quantities of radioactive substances which may be present in surrounding materials. But even when care is taken to eliminate all these contaminations there is still a residual background left, which is quite small, about 2 ion pairs per c.c. per second, but unmistakeable. The question of the origin of this radiation aroused interest in the early investigators, but it was not until 1912 that it was established that this radiation could not be of terrestrial origin. In that year a young Austrian physicist, Victor Hess, took off in a balloon with a detecting instrument to measure the intensity of the radiation at various altitudes. The balloon rose to 16,000 feet and he found that the radiation was there very much stronger than at sea-level. Hess concluded, therefore, that these radiations must enter our atmosphere from above. Later investigations have fully confirmed this view, and it was for this reason that they were given the name cosmic radiations.

In the following years many investigations were carried out to find out the composition of the cosmic radiation at various altitudes and various geographical latitudes. An enormous amount of information has been obtained, particularly since 1947, when a number of new particles were discovered in the cosmic radiation. These are the various mesons, $\mu$-mesons, $\pi$-mesons, $\tau$-mesons, etc., which we discussed in Chapter I. Most information about these mesons came from the study of photographic plates sent up to the upper regions of the atmosphere in balloons. This has revealed a great wealth of all sorts of radiations in the upper atmosphere and has shown that the radiations there consist predominantly of protons of very high energy, up to $10^{17}$ electron-volts, with a small number of helium nuclei and a still smaller fraction of nuclei of heavier elements. Although much is still not understood about the cosmic rays and, in particular, it is not yet clear what is the role of the various heavy mesons and what is their origin, yet the main features of cosmic radiations are well known.

The cosmic radiation as observed in the atmosphere is composed of three parts, *i.e.* electrons (positive and negative), $\mu$-mesons (positive and negative), and protons. There are also many $\gamma$-rays, or photons, but these are grouped with the electrons for reasons which will be explained presently. The variation of the intensity of these three components with the height in the atmosphere is shown in Fig. 21. The horizontal scale gives not the altitude directly but the atmospheric pressure; the zero of the scale corresponds to the top of the atmosphere. The vertical scale, which is a logarithmic scale, gives the intensity of the various components, expressed as the number of particles per cm.$^2$ per second per unit solid angle. It is seen that at the top of the atmosphere the proton component has the highest intensity, but, as protons are easily absorbed when passing through matter, this component becomes very quickly attenuated so that at sea level very little is left of it – it amounts there to less than $\frac{1}{2}$ per cent of the total intensity. The electron component is somewhat more penetrating, and at sea-level it accounts for about 25 per cent of the radiation. But the most penetrating is the μ-meson component which contributes most to the cosmic radiation at sea level, although it is the weakest component in the upper regions of the atmosphere. The most interesting fact is that both

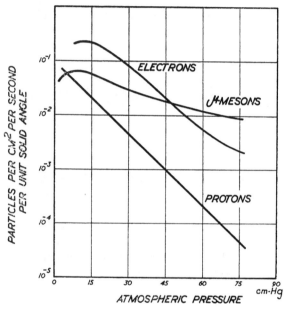

FIG. 21. *Composition of cosmic radiation at various altitudes.*

the electron and the μ-meson components actually decrease at the very top of the atmosphere. This can only happen if they are secondary radiations produced by some primary in the upper atmosphere. This primary radiation is most likely to be composed of protons and heavier nuclei which arrive from the outside and, hitting the atmosphere, give rise to μ-mesons and electrons.

If we make this assumption, that the primary radiation reaching us from the outside consists mainly of protons of very high energy, then it is easy to explain the variation of intensity of the various components in passing through the atmosphere. The primary protons, as soon as they reach the atmosphere, collide with the nuclei of oxygen and nitrogen, and in doing so give rise to the production of $\pi$-mesons. We know that this process occurs because it can be reproduced in the laboratory by means of the large accelerators. As we know (Table I), there are three types of $\pi$-mesons: positive, negative and neutral. All of them are very short-lived, but they interact with matter in different ways. Neutral $\pi$-mesons in passing through matter become annihilated and converted into $\gamma$-rays of high energy. The negatively charged $\pi$-mesons are attracted to nuclei through which they pass, giving rise to disintegrations, and very often breaking up the nucleus completely. Such events are, however, relatively rare and normally both negative and positive $\pi$-mesons, after coming to the end of their life, decay spontaneously into $\mu$-mesons and neutrinos. This process is, therefore, the origin of the $\mu$-meson component in cosmic radiation. M-mesons do not interact with nuclei and consequently they can pass a long distance through matter without much loss in intensity. However, the $\mu$-meson, too, is unstable and at the end of its life it breaks up into an electron and two neutrinos. We see now that the ultimate result of the passage of a primary radiation of protons through the atmosphere is the production of positive and negative $\mu$-mesons, positive and negative electrons, $\gamma$-rays and neutrinos.

*Cascade showers*

The detailed mechanism of the interactions with matter of the $\pi$- and $\mu$-mesons is not yet known; but the processes governing the passage of electrons and $\gamma$-rays through matter are now very well understood. An electron of low energy, in passing through matter, loses energy almost entirely through ionizing collisions, but for high-energy electrons another process becomes predominant, *i.e.* radiation. An electron passing through the field of a nucleus is decelerated and its energy is then converted into pure electromagnetic radiation, or 'photons'. In fact, the production of X-rays is based on this process; but while at electron energies of below 1 MeV it is a minor effect, it becomes the chief phenomenon at high energies. Such a high-energy electron in passing through matter will, therefore, give rise to high-energy photons or X-rays. A photon, of high energy, in passing through matter undergoes predominantly a materialization process, *i.e.* pair production, in which a photon is converted into a pair of positive and negative electrons. Thus a cascade process is obtained in which electrons give rise to photons and these in turn to electrons. Starting with one electron of high energy, it will soon lose some of its energy in passing through the field of an atom and produce a photon; the electron itself will carry on with less energy. The photon in turn will give rise to a pair of electrons. Thus, instead of one electron of high energy we now have three of lower energy. Each of these three can produce further photons, giving rise to further electrons, and so on. In this way the number of photons and electrons is rapidly increasing, and at the same time the energy of these particles is rapidly decreasing. Finally, a stage is reached when the energy of both the photons and the electrons is too small to produce further photons or electron pairs; the remaining energy is then dissipated in the usual way, by ionizing collisions and by ordinary scattering or the photo-electric effect.

The occurrence of such cascades in cosmic radiation has been definitely established; Plate X shows a cloud chamber photograph in which the occurrence of such a cascade shower was recorded. The cloud chamber contained a number of lead plates, each about 1·2 cm. thick, inserted in order to enable the electrons and photons to dissipate their energy more quickly than they would have done in a gas. The cascade starts on the top and it produces initially a small shower of a few electrons (the photons cannot be observed as they do not produce tracks). At this high energy the electrons produced move mainly in the forward direction and the shower is very narrow. In passing through the second plate some of the electrons are converted into photons, which in turn give rise to further electron pairs; the shower contains now more particles in it. This process is repeated in passing through the third and fourth plates; we see that the number of particles in the shower has greatly increased and also that the shower has now a larger spread. By that time the energy of the individual electrons and photons has already decreased a great deal so that the chance of producing further photons or electrons is much smaller; the shower now contains fewer particles with a still wider spread, until at the last plate very few electrons are left. The theory of these cascade showers has been worked out in great detail and accounts very well for the behaviour of the electron component in cosmic radiation.

*Origin of cosmic rays*

As has already been stated, the primary cosmic radiation is mainly composed of protons with a small proportion of α-particles and heavier nuclei. In fact, it appears that the composition of the primary cosmic radiation is very nearly the same as that of matter in the universe in general, *i.e.* mainly hydrogen, less helium and still less of the heavier elements.

This fact may have a very great bearing on the question of the origin of cosmic rays. Where do cosmic rays come from? Do they come from the sun or from some stars, or perhaps from outside our Galaxy?

It is perhaps necessary to establish first that cosmic rays really come from outside, and are not created somehow in the vicinity of our planet. This fact can be fairly easily decided by measuring the cosmic ray intensity at various geographical latitudes. As is known, the earth behaves like a magnet, it possesses a magnetic field and its lines of force run from the North Magnetic Pole to the South Magnetic Pole. It will also be remembered that a charged particle moving in a magnetic field is deflected from its path, the amount of this deflection depending on the energy of the particle and on its initial direction in relation to the magnetic field. The primary cosmic radiations consist of charged particles, and their paths, on approaching the earth, will be influenced by its magnetic field. Some particles which would have reached the earth in the absence of a magnetic field will be deflected away from it; others which would not have reached the earth will be directed towards it, and still others will be made to carry out complicated orbits around the earth. Although this problem is very complex it has been worked out in detail, and it was found that the cosmic radiation should show a definite latitude effect. The Pole should be reached by particles of all energies, but as we go towards the Equator particles of low energy should gradually be cut off, since a given latitude can be reached only by particles above a certain energy. If, therefore, the cosmic rays contain particles of various energies we should observe a diminution of the cosmic ray intensity as we move nearer the Equator. A survey of the cosmic radiation intensity in various parts of the world, carried out by Millikan and others, has indeed proved the existence of this geomagnetic effect. Both its variation with latitude and altitude agreed with the theory.

The geomagnetic effect proves that the primary radiation must come from outside the earth and that it consists mainly of particles of very high energy, most of which are above $15 \times 10^9$ eV. It further shows that these particles come in fairly uniformly from every direction in space.

Do the cosmic rays originate in our sun? At first sight this possibility seems to be eliminated by the fact that the cosmic radiation has about the same intensity both by day and by night. For, if it were of solar origin, we might have expected to see a much greater intensity of radiation coming from the direction of the sun than from any other direction. It has been pointed out, however, that in the region of space surrounding the sun there may exist irregular magnetic fields of sufficient strength to prevent or greatly retard the escape of cosmic rays. This trapping of cosmic rays by the magnetic field of the sun would destroy any original direction; and so they would appear to us to arrive from all directions. The main argument, however, against the solar origin is that we would have expected to find some correlation between cosmic ray intensity and the activity of the sun. Although it has been observed that large flares in the sun do cause a slight increase in the cosmic radiation on the earth, yet this effect is far too small. We must, therefore, conclude that at least the bulk of cosmic radiation reaches us from space outside the solar system.

Various suggestions have been put forward to explain the origin and composition of the primary cosmic radiation. It is possible that it originates in stars, particularly in the so-called supernovae. As will be explained in Chapter IX, supernovae are gigantic explosions which occur in our Galaxy once every few hundred years, releasing an amount of energy roughly equivalent to the total mass of the sun. It is possible that when a star has exhausted its supply of hydrogen and subsequently contracts due to gravitational forces it may reach a state of such great compression that the core is just one enormous lump of nuclear matter. The star would then blow up in a tremendous nuclear explosion, and its products, the nuclei of the heavy elements, disintegrating would eject protons, α-particles and other light nuclei. Even if cosmic rays were produced entirely in individual bursts several hundred years apart, we should still expect the observed cosmic ray intensity to be constant as the particles would circulate in the Milky Way for millions of years.

Another possibility, suggested by Fermi, is that particles in the inter-stellar dust are accelerated in a kind of cyclotron effect by the combination of the magnetic fields set up by stars and the radio-frequency fields from their own radiations. In such a way it may be possible to accelerate particles to extremely high energies. Another theory suggests that particles ejected by some such accelerating process are diffused through interstellar space, making collisions with cosmic dust and gradually gaining more and more energy.

At present there is not enough evidence in favour of any one of these speculations and the question of the origin of cosmic rays is still open. There can be no doubt, however, that cosmic ray research will eventually contribute not only to our knowledge of the structure of matter and the nature of nuclear forces but also to a better understanding of the structure of the whole universe. We shall return to this fascinating topic in Chapter IX.

# CHAPTER VI

# Matter and its properties

*Inter-atomic forces*

So far we have dealt only with single atoms, the elementary particles of which they are made, and the changes in structure which can occur in nuclear reactions and radioactivity. We have hardly mentioned the arrangement of the electrons in the outer parts of the atom, which determine how the atoms appear to each other. The importance of nuclear reactions today has tended to make us forget that only the 'minor' nuclear reactions associated with natural and artificial radioactivity were known before 1939, that is, before nuclear fission was discovered. Until that year the word 'reaction' would probably have been assumed to refer to chemical reactions, in which only the outermost parts of atoms are affected. In this chapter we deal with the interactions between whole atoms, which give rise to the familiar phenomena of chemistry and to the existence and behaviour of matter in bulk.

Perhaps the best starting-point in this discussion will be the assertion that every atom exerts a force upon every other atom. The details and the magnitude of the force vary as between one type of atom and another, but in general the force is always a force of attraction when the atoms are at a distance apart greater than their normal diameters, changing to a force of repulsion if the atoms are forced very close together. Thus there will be a tendency for atoms to draw together and 'stick'. This can be very conveniently illustrated in graphical form. In Fig. 22 we see a typical graph relating the potential energy of interaction of two atoms to the distance between their centres. It will be seen that the curve has been drawn so that the energy is zero at large distances. This is clearly a reasonable way of fixing the zero, or reference level, where we are dealing with energies of interaction,

because there will be no interaction at very large distances apart.
Then at smaller distances the energy adopts increasingly large
negative values until the curve eventually reaches a minimum and
turns upwards, finally reaching large positive values at very small
distances. Two atoms 'held' very close together (where the energy
of interaction is positive) would tend to fly apart if released. On
the other hand, if they were held at an appreciable distance
apart – but not so far apart that there was no perceptible inter-

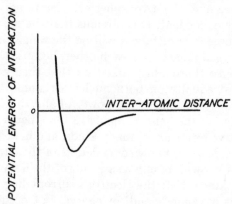

FIG. 22. *Potential energy of interaction of two atoms.*

action – they would tend to move together. When this curve is
examined by the methods of calculus (see Appendix) it turns out
that the slope at any point is equal to the net force of attraction.
Thus at large distances there is, as already explained, a force of
attraction, and at very small distances a force of repulsion. The
position at which these cancel each other out, so that there is
no net force, will be the normal relative position of the two
atoms when stuck together. This is clearly at the minimum – or
'trough' – where the slope is zero.

We must now try to understand something of the origin of
these inter-atomic forces, as far as is possible with our limited
equipment. Perhaps the easiest kind of force to understand is
the repulsive force which comes into play at small distances
apart. If there were no such repulsive force, atoms would not

have individual existence and would all merge into each other. So the very existence of discrete atoms is a *de facto* demonstration of the existence of repulsion. But we can see a possible origin of this force in the structure of the atom as a positively charged nucleus surrounded by a cloud of negative electrons. If we consider two such atoms approaching so closely together that they overlap greatly (assuming for the purposes of this argument that this does not cause any distortion of the individual atoms) we eventually arrive at a condition in which the two nuclei are very close together, and the two spherical electronic clouds have become nearly coincident. It is obvious that the most important force under these circumstances will be the repulsion of the two positively charged nuclei upon each other, because the electronic clouds will be so thoroughly mixed up that their contributions will act almost equally on both nuclei. At small distances the repulsion of nuclei becomes very powerful and this is, in part at least, the origin of the general repulsive force between atoms.

The attractive forces are of many kinds, and in order to understand them we have to know some details of the outer structure of atoms. It is known, mainly as a result of the detailed study of spectra of all kinds, that the electrons surrounding an atom do not behave as a vague 'cloud' of charge, but occupy, in some way, different zones at varying distances from the atomic nucleus. These zones are called shells, and they can be further divided into sub-shells. Further, there are certain favoured numbers for the occupation by electrons of these shells. Thus the innermost shell cannot hold more than two, the next outer shell not more than eight, leading to larger numbers for shells still further out. The chemical behaviour of atoms is then found to depend on whether the number of their electrons is sufficient to nearly fill, just fill, or overfill a particular one of these shells.

This can be explained by considering as examples three atoms, fluorine, neon, and sodium, which are adjacent in the Periodic Table of Elements (Fig. 3), according to their atomic numbers, having respectively 9, 10, and 11 outer electrons. In spite of being so close together in mass and nuclear charge, they are quite different in behaviour. Fluorine is a gas which reacts violently with everything with which it comes into contact – so violently indeed that it is only in recent years that it has been possible to study its chemical properties under controlled conditions. Neon is an 'inert gas', which can hardly be induced to enter into any chemical reaction; for this reason it can be used as a protective atmosphere in experiments at high temperatures. Sodium is a soft solid which reacts violently with water and is a constituent of many common compounds such as sodium chloride (common salt) and sodium bicarbonate (soda).

The clue to their behaviour is given by the case of neon. It has 10 electrons, sufficient to fill two electronic shells with 2 and 8 electrons respectively. It therefore has no tendency to lose or gain an electron, and this is the key to its remarkable chemical inertness. Fluorine, on the other hand, has a tendency under certain circumstances to gain an electron in order to fill a shell, in so doing becoming as a whole negatively charged, or ionized. Similarly, but conversely, sodium has a tendency to lose its extra electron, becoming as a whole positively charged.

Now we can consider the situation when a sodium atom and a fluorine atom find themselves within reasonable distance of each other. They can satisfy their needs to have just filled electronic shells by transferring the 'spare' electron from the sodium atom to the fluorine atom. The atoms have now become positively and negatively charged ions, respectively, and they will exert a purely electric force of attraction upon each other, which may lead to the formation of a molecule of sodium fluoride, or perhaps, if there are very many such pairs of atoms, to a solid lump of this substance.

It is not so easy to explain why, for example, fluorine atoms are hardly ever found singly, but always in pairs, as symbolized by $F_2$. This is an example of a different kind of attractive force which is of the greatest importance in chemistry. Again, we could not give a true explanation without use of some of the most difficult concepts in modern physics and chemistry (those of *quantum mechanics*), but we can give a rough explanation, and one which happens to coincide with that offered by chemists before the modern developments were understood. It is that the two fluorine atoms, each having 7 electrons in its outer shell, *share* one of these between them in order to achieve the full complement of 8. This is illustrated in the following 'equation' representing the formation of a molecule of fluorine from two atoms.

$$: \overset{..}{\underset{..}{F}} \cdot \; + \; \cdot \overset{..}{\underset{..}{F}} : \quad \rightarrow \quad : \overset{..}{\underset{..}{F}} : \overset{..}{\underset{..}{F}} :$$

It can readily be imagined that two atoms will find it increasingly difficult to share more than one electron, for simple geometrical reasons, although there may be no such reasons to prevent one atom sharing several of its electrons among two or more other atoms. Considerations such as these, involving the actual shapes of molecules, the different quantities of energy associated with the various electronic arrangements, and particularly the actual shapes of the orbits in which the electrons are supposed to be localized, make up a large part of modern chemistry when viewed properly in the light of modern concepts rather than in the rough way adopted here.

We must now consider the attraction between atoms of neon or other inert gases (argon, krypton, etc.), and the question of how there may be an attractive force between *molecules* such as $F_2$ in spite of the fact that the atoms of the molecule have, at least to a first approximation, satisfied their own requirements. There are various kinds of force involved, all much weaker than those already mentioned, and therefore called secondary forces, as compared with the strong primary forces between 'unsatisfied' or unsaturated atoms. The attraction between these atoms or molecules are essentially due to forces between electric dipoles – the electric analogues of ordinary magnets. Two magnets will always attract or repel one another, and if one or both can rotate freely they will adopt a position which makes the force attractive. The characteristic of an ordinary magnet is that there is an apparent separation of magnetic poles (the analogues of electric charges) to the two ends. Although, in an electrically neutral atom such as the neon atom there is no separation of electric charge, there are temporary fluctuations in the distribution of charge which give rise to temporary dipoles. One such dipole will act upon a neighbouring atom in much the same way as one magnet causes another to rotate, so that there is a temporary attraction. It will

always be an attraction, whatever the direction of the original
dipole, and there is, in fact, a steady though relatively weak
attraction between any such pair of atoms or between atoms and
molecules, or between pairs of molecules. In some molecules there
may be permanent dipoles arising from shape and the actual
separation of charge during the formation of the molecule, and
here the 'secondary' forces of attraction are somewhat stronger.
The difference between the effects of the temporary dipoles in
non-polar molecules, as they are called, and of the permanent
dipoles in polar molecules, can be noted in many familiar phenomena. For example, benzene and water do not mix. Liquid benzene exists because of non-polar attractive forces, liquid water
because of polar forces; the attraction of the water molecules for
each other is so much greater than, say, of a water molecule for
a benzene molecule, that benzene molecules are, so to speak,
'squeezed out' of the neighbourhood of water. Attempts to mix
the two liquids by violent shaking result only in a collection of
separate droplets of benzene and water.

Finally, there is an attraction between metallic atoms, which
differs from those already discussed. (It cannot be explained in
simple terms, but only with the help of modern quantum theory.
The reader may perhaps be asked to take this on trust, with the
assurance that he has many allies even among physicists and
chemists in this.) A characteristic example is provided by
metallic sodium. Here the 'spare' electrons, one from each atom,
appear to be shared among all the sodium atoms, and act to bind
them together strongly.

These main kinds of inter-atomic attraction or cohesive force
are not often found in 'pure' form. Most substances cohere because of a mixture of contributions from several of these forces.
However, many theoretical physicists would prefer not to speak
in this way of inter-atomic forces as pure or mixed, but would
regard them all as manifestations of particular ways in which
electrons can distribute themselves over one, two, or more atoms.
As we shall see in the next chapter, the theoretical problem is not
simple, because the relatively simple laws governing ordinary
electric and magnetic behaviour do not apply on the atomic
scale.

*Chemical behaviour*

We have seen that chemical behaviour depends essentially on the precise arrangement of electrons and that there are certain number relationships in these arrangements. At one stroke this discovery gave reality to the conjectures of generations of chemists. For it had been known for many years that chemical behaviour had a periodic distribution among the elements. In the Periodic Table, groups of elements of similar chemical behaviour are picked out by tabulating the elements in a number of columns (Fig. 3).

Thus the tendencies of different atoms towards particular types of chemical behaviour are in principle understood, although the degree of complexity of molecules makes theoretical prediction difficult. Some of the complex molecules now known, particularly those encountered in biology and in the new field of chemical industry associated with 'plastics', may contain thousands of atoms.

We next wish to understand why chemical reactions are so common, that is, why molecules can sometimes interchange atoms and form new substances, and why molecules already formed can sometimes dissociate again into separate atoms. The answer is to be found by considering in rather more detail the significance of the energy relationships involved and the role of temperature. Without defining temperature rigorously, we can assert that the most important consequence of change of temperature is that the amount of energy associated with an atom, molecule, crystal, droplet, or other system changes in the same sense. High temperature means high energy and low temperature low energy, although in any collection of atoms or molecules the different particles do not all have the same energy; there is a distribution of energies over a range (see, for example, Fig. 19). In a gas, for example, the average kinetic energy and the average velocity will be higher at high temperatures. The tendency of a pair of atoms to approach to the distance of lowest energy of interaction will clearly be affected by what the temperature actually is. If we consider as an example a mixture of sodium and fluorine at such a high temperature that both elements are gaseous, we can safely assert that there will be molecules of sodium fluoride present *and* free sodium and fluorine. Then at higher temperatures the proportion of free sodium and fluorine will increase. Also, the proportion of the fluorine which is in the form of single atoms rather than in molecules ($F_2$) will increase at high temperatures. The precise composition of such a mixture could in fact be worked out if we knew all the quantities of energy actually involved.

In more complex chemical reactions in which atoms are interchanged between molecules there are more quantities of energy to be considered. There are the energies which have to be supplied before the separate molecules can be dissociated (corresponding in a simple case to the depth of the potential trough in Fig. 22) and also the energies gained by formation of the new types of molecule. Even in a gaseous mixture there will be ample opportunity for interchanges during collisions between molecules. The course of a given chemical reaction will depend on all these quantities of energy and upon the temperature, and also on the concentrations in which the various substances are present. In principle the problem of deciding which reactions will actually occur is well understood by chemists. In practice it is of course complex, but fortunately there are methods by which many of the relevant quantities of energy can be measured directly. The question is of such great importance in industries based on chemistry that the effort to understand them, using this semi-theoretical approach, has proved very worth while.

### The solid state

As has already been mentioned, inter-atomic attraction can cause atoms to condense into large lumps of matter as well as into molecules. The body of knowledge which has grown up about the actual arrangement of atoms in solids is now so immense that it is surprising to recall that almost nothing was known about it before the First World War. Most of the information has been derived by the use of X-rays, whose wavelength is of the same order as the normal diameter of an atom. We have not the space to discuss the methods used and must merely give the results; we should remark, however, that they depend on observing regularities in the spacing of atoms rather than on making observations of the positions of single atoms. The photograph, taken by X-rays, which the X-ray structure analyst obtains and studies, contains a number of spots, curves, or lines, each referring to a particular regularity in spacing, and he has to interpret them by complex methods. These X-ray pictures are of course quite different from those used in medical diagnosis, which depend merely on the differing transparency of different substances to X-rays. A familiar observation which points to the basis of these methods is the pattern which can be seen when a street lamp is viewed through the fine and regular cotton network of an umbrella cover.

Starting with the simplest structures, we now describe some of the ways in which solids are built up. The structures of the solidified inert 'gases' (neon, argon, etc.) and of metals such as copper (in which there is one extra electron above a completed shell) turn out to be very simple. For the force of attraction between these atoms acts equally in all directions; it has no special directional tendency. The structure is then determined only by the requirement that each atom should be as close to its neighbours as possible. In fact, two arrangements which give the closest possible packing of spheres – that is, which pack more spheres into a given volume than any other arrangement – are adopted by these solids. Some features of these 'close-packed' structures are illustrated in Fig. 23 and can be easily understood with the help of a few marbles or ball-bearings. If we start by laying marbles on a flat surface as in (a), so that each marble touches six neighbours and is at the centre of the regular hexagon formed by the lines joining their centres, we have correctly imitated one of the basic features of these structures – the arrangement within certain crystal 'planes'. (It is advisable to deposit this layer in a 'tray' or other container which will keep the marbles in close contact with each other.) We proceed to build up the model of the crystal in three dimensions by superimposing one such plane layer on another. If we drop a marble somewhere upon the first layer, it will naturally take up a position in one of the hollows formed between the marbles of this layer. The positions to be adopted by all other marbles in the second layer are then determined, as shown by broken lines in (b). Now in placing the third layer upon the second we find there

are two possibilities. We start by placing a marble in one of the
hollows formed between the marbles of the second layer. With
respect to the second layer there is nothing to choose between
any of the hollows, but if we look at the possible positions with
the first layer still in mind it is found that the new marble can
either be placed immediately above a marble in the first layer,
or in another position which is not directly above any marble in
the two layers already deposited. If the first position is adopted,
the new layer is really equivalent to the first layer and we can

(a)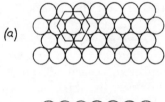

(b)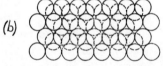

Fig. 23. (a) and (b) Models
illustrating the building of
close-packed structures.

describe the method of putting down the successive layers by the
symbol 121212. If the second position is adopted the lateral
position of the third layer can be identified as 3, and the method
of deposition described as 123123. This of course implies that
the fourth layer is put with its centres immediately above those
of the first layer, and it follows from what has been said that it
could obviously have its centres above those of the second layer.
In fact, except for mistakes (which do sometimes occur!) the
natural arrangements are 121212 ... and 123123 ... For the
arrangement in a real crystal – made of atoms, not of marbles –
does not depend on putting down layers in this somewhat casual
way, but is determined by the actual amounts of energy involved

E

in the forces between atoms, and these forces extend to atoms at a distance of several layer thicknesses.

If the reader has carried out the experiment, he may note several features of interest about his pile of marbles which are very difficult to illustrate in two-dimensional figures. First, each marble touches twelve neighbours; this is the maximum number of spheres which another sphere of the same size can be made to touch. Secondly, there are many other layers now discernible in the model, inclined at various angles to the layers put down. With care, he might be able to make the upper parts of the model slide horizontally relative to the lower layers; and he can perhaps imagine how in a real crystal sliding might be able to occur in several directions. This is a rough imitation of what happens when a metal wire is severely stretched!

It is perhaps surprising that typical and very common metallic structures can be imitated so easily. There is one other which is more difficult to illustrate, in which each atom has only eight close neighbours, situated relative to itself as the corners of a cube are to the centre, but six other neighbours not too far away, being at the centres of the six adjacent cubes which share corners with its own cube. This arrangement is known as the 'body-centred cubic' structure. In this case the advantage (in energy) of having the further six neighbours offsets the disadvantage of having only eight very close neighbours. Which of the three arrangements is adopted by a particular metal cannot yet be predicted in detail. The differences in energy between them are very small compared with the total energy of interaction and such fine details are at present beyond the reach of theoretical prediction.

*Crystals*

The word 'crystal' has already been used here and it may be that it has previously signified to the reader something like a diamond, or quartz crystal, with smooth faces and sharp edges – quite unlike his pile of marbles. But the real significance of the term crystal is that it implies an internal regularity of structure such as illustrated in these examples. The shape of the model as a whole is not very relevant, being superficial in more senses than one. How then is our model related to the actual arrangement in, say, a lump of metal? The answer is that a piece of metal is normally made up of a large number of crystals oriented in all directions at random, but firmly stuck to each other. If we choose a line perpendicular to the tray upon which the marbles are laid as defining the characteristic direction or orientation for the particular crystal model, then there will be such lines pointing in all directions in a correspondingly large-scale model of a lump of metal.

This polycrystalline structure, as it is called, is characteristic of metals. It arises in the first place usually because the lump of metal is formed by the freezing of molten metal. This process starts at a very large number of points within the liquid and the crystals, beginning with varying orientations, grow until they meet each other. It is possible by careful preparation of a metallic surface to see the individual grains with the help of a microscope. A typical photograph is shown in Plate XXII in which the separate grains, each having an irregular shape, can be clearly seen. The average size of a single grain might be about $10^{-4}$ cm. – or about $10^4$ atomic diameters – in length or breadth. The fact that they are then able to stick firmly together, in spite of the discontinuities in arrangement which must exist at the crystal boundaries, is mainly due to the generally non-directional character of the inter-atomic attraction. This is also the reason why alloys, or solutions of different metals in each other, can exist over such a wide range of compositions. As would be expected, the inert 'gases' can also be solidified into polycrystalline lumps, because their inter-atomic attractions are also non-directional.

Although one cannot normally say anything about the crystalline structure of a lump of metal by looking at it with the naked eye, it is possible by special techniques to make neighbouring crystals grow at the expense of each other until, ultimately, the whole volume is occupied by a single crystal which has, so to speak, 'eaten up' all the others. The properties of these large metallic single crystals are extremely interesting. For example, if a bar consisting of one crystal is severely stretched, markings appear on the surface (Fig. 24) which suggest that during the extension of the bar sliding has occurred on a number of parallel planes in the crystal. In the early studies on such specimens it was puzzling to the experimenters to find that the bars were sometimes brittle and sometimes quite tough. But when the specimens were studied by X-ray methods it was realized that the crystal orientations differed from one bar to another, and that the behaviour of a particular bar must depend on whether a plane upon which easy sliding could occur was inclined suitably with respect to the direction of the force applied. If it could not slide easily, then it might break completely along some other plane. Of course, if the large crystal is obtained by a method which depends upon one crystal eating up all the others, it is hardly possible to decide at the start which crystal will win.

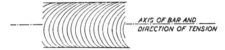

Fig. 24. *Appearance of slip-lines on a single crystal.*

Turning from the simplest structures we proceed to describe the main features of the ionic crystal. The most characteristic and common example is sodium chloride, or common salt. This is made up of positively charged sodium atoms, or ions, and negatively charged chlorine ions. The determining factor here is that ions of opposite charge attract each other but ions of like charge repel each other. Each ion, therefore, tries to surround itself by as many as possible of its opposite numbers and to keep away from ions of its own kind. The result is shown in Fig. 25, in which the ions have been represented by circles whose diameter is small in comparison with their distance apart. This is not done in order to suggest that the atoms in ionic crystals are more openly spaced than in metals, but only in order that the arrangement in three dimensions can be more easily understood. In reality, the ions must still be imagined as quite closely packed together. In such a crystal we cannot anywhere see a 'molecule' of sodium chloride, as would be represented by NaCl, where Na stands for a sodium atom and Cl for a chlorine atom. No single sodium atom belongs to a single chlorine atom; they all belong to each other. It might perhaps be said that the whole crystal is now a molecule, if one likes to think in chemical terms.

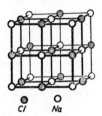

Fɪɢ. 2 5. *The sodium chloride structure.*

The 'rock-salt' structure, as this is called, is probably the simplest ionic crystal structure. In general, however, the structures of ionic crystals cannot be as simple as those of metallic crystals, for there are always at least two kinds of atom to be accommodated and they may be of differing size. Indeed, quite complex

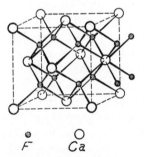

Fɪɢ. 26. *The structure of calcium fluoride.*

structures are very soon found, particularly if there are more than two. The structure of calcium fluoride ($CaF_2$) is illustrated in Fig. 26. Calcium normally has two electrons over the complement of the largest filled shell and thus has a tendency to form doubly charged ions. Since the ions of fluorine can be only singly charged there must be twice as many fluorine ions as calcium ions in order to preserve the net balance of charge. The degree of complexity occasioned by this rather simple requirement is rather striking; the structure is already more complicated than one can easily apprehend.

As might be expected from the selective nature of the inter-atomic attraction, ionic crystals do not easily stick to each other and polycrystalline lumps of such substances do not occur. Large crystals can however be grown from solutions, or sometimes from the molten substance, and they usually have the characteristic 'crystal' appearance in which plane faces and sharp edges can be seen. As has already been seen from the example of the pile of marbles, there are very many identifiable 'planes' in a crystal. Which planes come to the fore and are seen in the finished crystal of regular shape is a matter which may depend upon differences between the rates of growth in different directions. A curious fact is that the shape or 'habit' of natural crystals found in the ground may differ according to the locality. This is because minute traces of other substances, which may or may not be present in the locality, can sometimes become attracted pre-ferentially towards particular faces of a growing crystal and inhibit growth in a particular direction.

As soon as we consider elements in which the 'electron-sharing' type of force is important, even more complex structures are found. For there is a directional tendency in this type of force. The atom behaves as if it had a particular number of arms (or bonds, as they are usually called) reaching out in particular directions. Except for a small number of crystals such as diamond (consisting only of carbon atoms) in which the requirements of each atom as to the preferred number and position of its neigh-bours can be satisfied exactly, the tendency is towards more and more complex structures, whose elucidation requires all the art and skill of the X-ray crystallographer. In some crystals mole-cules occupy sites in the crystal framework (or lattice) just as atoms or ions do in other crystals. Structures can indeed be encountered which depend for their geometrical arrangement on all the considerations mentioned above in the course of discussion of the different kinds of inter-atomic force.

## Properties of crystals

Let us now consider briefly some properties of crystals of the types so far described. As soon as the structures of the simpler ionic crystals became known, physicists tried to work out 'theoretical' values for various measurable properties in order to compare them with the known measured values. In the case of sodium chloride, for instance, the charges and distance apart of the ions are known and it might be expected that one could work out accurately the magnitude of the inter-atomic attraction. This leads fairly directly to an estimate of the compressibility or other elastic properties of the crystal. Theoretical and experimental physicists devoted much attention to the case of sodium chloride and arrived at the following surprising conclusions: while the experimental and theoretical values of the compressibility agreed quite well, there were serious discrepancies in the estimates of the force required to cause sliding of one plane over another and of the force required to cause complete fracture – both obviously within the scope of suitable mathematical treatments. It appeared that similar discrepancies existed for all solids and that, in fact, solids could show large deformations or fracture under forces very much smaller (by factors as high as 1,000 in some cases) than expected. Single crystals in particular were exceptionally 'soft' and weak.

The complete answer to these anomalies does not yet exist, but they are known to be intimately connected with 'defects' or faults of many kinds which can exist in crystals. Indeed, the diagram of Fig. 24 has already given one clue. For in the specimen illustrated sliding has obviously occurred only on quite widely separated and preferentially chosen planes. The spacing between 'steps' is at least of the order of hundreds or thousands of atomic diameters. In some way these planes must offer reduced resistance to sliding.

A great deal of ingenuity has recently been devoted to this problem by suggesting ways in which defects such as 'missing' atoms, 'extra' atoms or missing or extra lines of atoms, as well as defects of many other kinds, can affect the mechanical properties. It is easy to demonstrate one way in which a defect can reduce the strength by cutting a notch at the edge of a strip of paper with a pair of scissors. This reduces greatly the force required to tear the strip in two. The grain boundary is a particularly important factor since it might be expected to offer resistance to sliding and to fracture because of the sudden change of orientation of planes in the crystal. It is certainly true that the introduction of more and more boundaries by reducing the grain size increases both the resistance to stretching and the ultimate strength of metals. This is why such processes as rolling and forging are carried out in the manufacture of metals. The severe deformations which these cause break down the crystals into smaller and smaller grains, ultimately reaching a limit because of the inherent tendency of the metal to 'heal' up to a certain grain-size. The metallographic examination of surfaces in order to obtain pictures such as that of Plate XXII is very important to the metallurgist since it enables him to find whether the grains in a metal specimen are of uniform size and whether the size is that desired.

Graphite is an interesting substance in its mechanical properties. It has strong cohesion within certain atomic planes but weak cohesion between the planes. Sliding of these planes relative to each other gives rise to its 'slippery' characteristics.

*Disordered structures*

Although crystallinity, that is, the existence of a regular or ordered internal structure extending at least over thousands of normal inter-atomic distances, has usually been considered the characteristic feature of the solid state, it is surprising to find how few of the common materials fit easily into this category. What are the structures of paper, wool, plastics, rubber, glass, coal? And what are typical structures of biological systems? X-ray methods have been increasingly used in recent years upon the study of these materials, and it is known that they all contain, to a greater or less extent, amorphous or disordered matter, lacking the characteristic ordered arrangement of crystals. The key to many of these structures lies in the ability of carbon atoms to take part in extremely long molecules having a chain character. Indeed, the study of the compounds of carbon, which is in itself a major fraction of chemistry, has been given the name organic chemistry because of the importance of this element in biological organisms. As we have seen in the case of diamond, carbon atoms behave as if they have four bonds reaching out towards other atoms. This can lead to a chain of the kind suggested by

$$
\begin{array}{cccc}
| & | & | & | \\
- \text{C} - \text{C} - \text{C} - \text{C} - \\
| & | & | & |
\end{array}
$$

in which each carbon atom takes part while still having two bonds to spare. Other atoms or groups of atoms can attach themselves to these to form substances of very many different kinds. A very common example is polythene, now used for electrical insulation and for kitchen ware, in which two hydrogen atoms are attached to each carbon atom. Other well-known substances depending upon such chains or upon rather more complex chain structures are cellulose, nylon, rubber.

Chain molecules can be many thousands of atoms in length and it is upon this fact that very much of the behaviour of these substances depends. These molecules are so long and complex that often they simply cannot fit themselves into any ordered arrangement. A lump of such a substance is just a bundle of chain molecules, as illustrated schematically in two dimensions in Fig. 27 (a). The bundle stays together partly because the molecules are to some extent knotted, or tangled, and partly because they are in any case 'sticky' through the inter-atomic attraction of secondary types, acting at a very large number of points. Often very high strength is found in these substances (in cotton and nylon, for instance); they sometimes appear not to suffer from weakening effects as do crystals and to exhibit values of strength which correspond to the real force required to pull chain molecules apart.

High polymers, or plastics, are of this general type or of that shown in Fig. 27 (b). Here cross-links are established between the atomic or molecular groups of different chains and the structure becomes three-dimensionally braced. Such materials (of which Bakelite is an example) are on the whole more likely to be brittle than those of class (a). In some substances there is an intermediate structure in which a greater or less amount of local regularity is found, as illustrated in Fig. 27 (c). Over small regions the chains lie approximately parallel but other regions are again oriented at random. An interesting case is that of rubber, in which the development of such ordered regions (or 'micelles') can be clearly seen in the X-ray picture when the rubber is stretched. If the rubber is allowed to recover its normal shape they disappear.

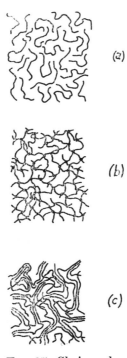

(a)

(b)

(c)

Fig. 27. *Chain mole-
cules:*
(a) *without cross
links;*
(b) *with cross links;*
(c) *with ordered
regions.*

## Liquids and gases

When a solid is heated to high temperatures the average energy of the atoms or molecules increases progressively. At first this energy is associated with increased vibration about the normal

sites, but at sufficiently high temperatures, the atoms or molecules break away entirely from each other and their energy is
then mainly the kinetic energy of motion. This is the gaseous
state of aggregation of matter. The temperature to which the
solid has to be heated, or conversely, the temperature to which
a gas has to be cooled before it will solidify, depends upon the
strength of the inter-atomic attraction. The inert gases do not
solidify until quite low temperatures have been reached, whilst
some metals remain solid until very high temperatures.

To a first approximation there is no energy of interaction in a
gas unless it is highly compressed, and most of the properties of
gases can be deduced theoretically by treating the atoms or
molecules as hard particles flying about constantly and making
collisions with each other and with the walls of the containing
vessel. If there is no vessel or other containing agent (such as
the gravitational force of the earth upon its atmosphere) the gas
expands indefinitely.

Most solids first melt into the liquid state before becoming
gaseous. This is not true under all circumstances, as we shall see
shortly, and it is convenient for the moment to consider the case
of the solid-gas transformation such as is ordinarily observed
with, say, solid carbon dioxide (a substance often used in the
storage of ice-cream). It is hardly sufficient to regard the above
statements as explaining the difference between solid and gas. It
is also necessary to understand why a quantity of a given solid
·and a quantity of its gas can be in equilibrium with each other at
a certain pressure and temperature – the pressure depending upon
the temperature – even though they do not have the same energy
per molecule, and energy in the form of heat has to be supplied to
convert more of the solid into gas. This is one of the most puzzling
facts of elementary physics. That is, we might have expected that
the change from solid to gas would consist essentially of an exchange between the potential energy of the solid and the kinetic
energy of the gas. The problem is solved in the science of thermodynamics, which concerns the relationships between heat and
other forms of energy. We find that it is not simply the energy
which determines the conditions of equilibrium in such cases. We
have, of course, to take the energy into account, as we did in dis-

cussing the inter-atomic distance at which atoms would find themselves in equilibrium with each other. But we must also take into account the tendency, in nature, for systems to become disordered if given the opportunity. It is possible to set up a measure of the disorder of a system using a quantity called the entropy and usually given the symbol $S$. When a solid and its gas are in equilibrium with each other at a given pressure and temperature, it is found that the so-called 'free energy' must be the same for both (for, say, unit mass of each). The free energy is given by the expression $H-TS$, where $T$ is the absolute temperature, and $H$ is the quantity of heat which would have to be put into a given system to raise it from the absolute zero to the given temperature at the given pressure.

We now see, by inspection of this expression, which is a difference between two terms, why a gas with high energy and high disorder (or entropy) can be in equilibrium with a solid, having lower energy and lower disorder. Further, we see that there must be a general tendency of all matter, as the temperature is increased, to become more disordered as well as more energetic.

Liquids are intermediate between solids and gases in their disorder. It will be useful to study the typical phase-equilibrium diagram of ordinary substances, illustrated in Fig. 28, which defines more precisely than we have so far done under what conditions the solid, liquid or gaseous state is found in a particular case. The lines of this diagram define the relationships between the particular pressures and temperatures at which pairs of phases can be in equilibrium. Thus the line labelled solid-vapour tells us the pressure at which solid and vapour are in equilibrium at any temperature. The areas between the lines then represent a range of pressures and temperatures at which only one phase exists. (For simplicity we ignore certain distinctions made between the terms 'vapour' and 'gas'.) Familiar ideas about change of phase – that heating causes solid to turn into liquid and liquid into gas – can be seen to be valid only within a certain range of pressures. For carbon dioxide, the line corresponding to atmospheric pressure would be below the point at which all three lines meet (the triple point) and the solid then turns directly into gas.

Another point to note in this figure is the critical point. It will be seen that above a certain pressure the distinction between liquid and gas disappears and the only change of phase which takes place is that from solid into gas – or it is better to use the term 'fluid', since the material is in a state which cannot be identified definitely as liquid or gas. Of course, when both liquid and gas are present it is easy to identify which is which since the liquid is denser and falls to the bottom. When only one phase

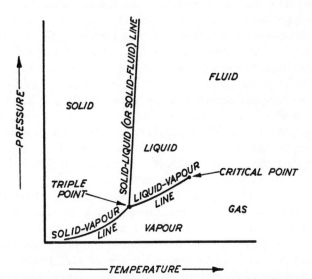

FIG. 28. *Phase-equilibrium diagram of a simple substance.*

exists, however, one cannot always be certain what to call it since a highly compressed gas has the same kind of molecular arrangement as a liquid. Such a highly compressed gas is of course very different from the 'ideal' gas, in which no inter-atomic attraction exists.

The physicist is not interested only in the behaviour of matter at atmospheric pressure. He can create pressures in the laboratory as high as 10,000 or even 100,000 atmospheres in order to study the more general behaviour of matter. He then finds that the solid-fluid line of Fig. 28 continues upward indefinitely to higher and higher pressures. This might be thought to reduce somewhat the importance of the true liquid state, which now can be seen to have a separate existence over only a relatively small range of pressures and temperatures; it is necessary, however, to try to understand how liquids, or highly compressed gases, differ from solids and from rarefied gases. The difference, as has already been implied, is in the degree of order. X-ray studies show that no regularity can be detected over a range greater than one or two atomic diameters; there is only the short-range order consequent upon the fact that the atoms or molecules have more or less precisely defined sizes and shapes. The complete explanation of the form of Fig. 28 would be very complex; in particular, there is not yet real agreement as to why there exists a critical point above which the liquid and gaseous states merge but apparently no corresponding critical point above which solid and fluid merge. This is bound up with the fact that there is a large gap between the longest range over which regularity (or order) can ever be detected in a liquid and the smallest range over which it is found in a solid – the grain-size of the finest polycrystalline aggregate.

The most characteristic property of liquids is their viscous flow. In a liquid there is a resistance to flow, or viscosity, if the flow entails relative motion between adjacent layers. In a tube, for instance, there is resistance because the layer touching the wall is at rest and layers nearer the centre are in motion. It is found that the force required to maintain a given speed of relative motion is proportional to the speed. This is perhaps the fundamental problem which must be explained by any theory of the liquid state. In a qualitative way it is easy to understand how it arises if we think of the flow in a liquid as being due to the 'rolling' of molecules or atoms around each other under the action of the applied force. It follows also if we think of a liquid as being a polycrystalline solid of very small grain-size (very much smaller than the smallest grain-size ever found in a real polycrystalline specimen) and recall that even in such a solid there is a tendency to 'heal' where grains are severely deformed or broken up by deformations.

Glass is especially interesting because it is structurally almost exactly the same as certain types of liquid, having no long-range order. This accounts for many of its properties, such as its transparency and its capacity to soften progressively when heated. Of course in its ordinary properties it behaves as a brittle solid rather than an ordinary liquid. However, when its behaviour is examined in detail it is found that many of its properties are more typical in kind, though not in magnitude, of liquids rather than of solids. In particular, the smallest force will cause glass to 'flow' if sufficient time is allowed (even though years might be required before a measurable amount of flow occurs) and this is typically liquid behaviour. The anomalous status of glass is then explained by saying that the difference between a glass and an ordinary liquid is that its viscosity is much greater – by a factor of perhaps $10^{22}$ at ordinary temperatures.

# CHAPTER VII

## From classical to modern physics

### Classical physics

The structure of physics at the end of the 19th century, which is more or less coincident with that part of the subject now usually known as 'classical physics', presented an impressive – and apparently impregnable – façade to the scientist of the day. Indeed, it was often asserted that physics was coming to an end! The overthrow of this complacent idea has been so complete that physicists will probably refrain in future from repeating the error.

Before proceeding to extra-terrestrial questions we trace in this chapter the main direction taken by physics as a whole since the end of its classical period. Not only will this dispel any suggestion that the only developments of note have been in atomic or nuclear physics, but it should also help the reader in his understanding of what is said in the other chapters of this book and guide him toward a unified view of natural phenomena.

Classical physics had indeed achieved a remarkable synthesis. The laws of mechanics, combined with Newton's law of gravitation, accounted for the motions of the planets and stars with almost perfect completeness. The laws of electromagnetism were adequate to account for all ordinary electric and magnetic phenomena and had predicted the existence of electromagnetic waves. By 1887 it had been shown that such waves existed, and later it was shown that they travelled with the same velocity as that of ordinary light. Indeed, by the turn of the century a great deal of the complete 'spectrum' of electromagnetic waves, illustrated in Fig. 29, had been investigated.

In spite of their almost complete ignorance of the properties of individual atoms, workers in the branch of physics known as 'statistical mechanics' had been able to make use of the atomic hypothesis in order to account for the most important properties of gases (in the kinetic theory of gases), and to a large extent for thermodynamic laws. This was achieved by combining the principles of mechanics with certain mathematical methods similar to those used by statisticians or insurance companies who have to deal with large populations. There was certainly good reason to feel that most of the natural phenomena known to physics had

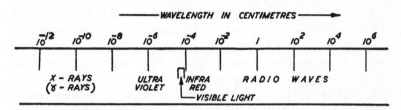

FIG. 29. *Range of electromagnetic radiation.*

been neatly identified, labelled, and correctly arranged in relation to each other.

Nevertheless, there was no real synthesis between mechanics and the study of matter. Physicists were also somewhat self-conscious about the lack of synthesis between mechanics and electromagnetism. For while all other known types of wave, such as transverse waves on stretched strings or longitudinal sound-waves in air, required a *medium* for their transmission, electromagnetic waves could travel through a vacuum. The difficulty had been so acutely felt that the term 'ether' had been coined for a hypothetical medium, of which no properties could be discovered besides its ability to transmit electromagnetic waves.

Let us now see how the cracks in the façade were prised open and how, with the simultaneous growth of atomic and nuclear knowledge, physics has been remoulded into a new and stronger unity.

## *Relativity*

The theoretical structure developed by Einstein and usually known by the term 'relativity' is very little understood by the public, although highly popular. In a sense it exemplifies the layman's concept of science as being somewhat absurd, since it can apparently lead to such statements as the assertion that the mass of a body can vary with its velocity, or that there is no such thing as simultaneity. In the hands of some writers on popular science the apparently fantastic aspects of Einstein's discoveries have been purposely stressed, whereas it should be emphasized that the ideas of relativity constitute no more than a sober recognition of certain observed facts of nature.

The problem which Einstein set out to solve concerned the 'ether', which was supposed to transmit light and other electro-magnetic waves. What was the state of motion, if any, of the ether? It seemed unlikely in the extreme that the ether could always be moving exactly with the earth and so it must have some velocity, relative to the earth, which would be expected to differ according to the position of the earth in its orbit around the sun. Now according to classical ideas, the transmission of any kind of wave-motion occurs with a characteristic velocity *relative to the medium*; to any observer moving relative to the medium (such as an observer on a moving ship studying the velocities of waves on water) the velocity would appear to be different. So the velocity of light would be expected to differ in different directions upon the earth, according to the direction and velocity of the 'ether wind' at the time. (We are only concerned here with the velocity of light in vacuum, not with the changes in the velocity which occur when light passes through a transparent material, and which give rise to the phenomenon of refraction.) This would have many consequences which could be tested by observation. In 1887, the American scientists Michelson and Morley, in one of the most famous experiments ever performed, made a direct test of the proposition that the velocity of light might vary according to the direction of transmission. They used a most sensitive and delicate optical instrument developed for the purpose, in which a direct comparison could be made of the velocities of light in two perpendicular directions. This could have detected easily a differ-ence equal in magnitude to the velocity of the earth in its orbit (about one ten-thousandth of the velocity of light). The result was entirely negative. Indeed, without now discussing all the other possible ways in which an ether wind might have been detected, it can be asserted that no generally accepted observations have ever been made which indicate that it exists.

It thus appears that if we have, say, a beam of light passing across two observation stations, its velocity will appear to be the same when measured at either station, whether or not the stations are moving relative to each other. This is the central dilemma. Einstein's proposal was that we accept this assertion as a starting-point and examine its implications. It very soon becomes obvious that these must extend far beyond the original proposition. For all kinds of idealized experiments can be devised by which the assertion might be tested. These may involve mechanical or electrical devices, and we know that in every experiment something will prevent the observers at the two stations from finding different values in their measurements of the velocity of the beam of light. One might imagine, for example, that motion alters the length of a rule or the timekeeping of a clock, so that the two observers moving relative to each other would be working with apparently dissimilar apparatus. This apparently rather fanciful suggestion points to the way in which the theory was actually developed.

Einstein then postulated that not only the velocity of light but *all* the laws of physics would be the same in all laboratories, whatever their motion. In particular, if two laboratories were moving relative to each other, observers in the two laboratories would find the laws of physics to be identical. We use the term 'laboratory' to describe a station at which there would be rules, clocks, electrical instruments, or other apparatus, which could have been standardized against each other. In fact, Einstein at first considered this principle to hold only for uniform relative motions – in the special theory of relativity of 1905. Later he extended it to cover motions which might include acceleration – in the general theory of relativity.

Now although it was postulated that physical laws would be the same in every laboratory, this did not mean that the physical laws already discovered were to be considered as of such perfect generality; it has already been seen in discussing the dilemma of the motion of the ether that this cannot be so. On the contrary, it appeared that many of the physical laws already in use had to be slightly modified, and only in their modified form did they obey Einstein's postulate. The procedure by which they were modified consisted of devising imaginary (or 'ideal') experiments – often of the kind which might earlier have been thought suitable for the purpose of looking for an ether wind – and making certain mathematical adjustments in order to remove the discrepancy suggested by the older laws, so as to bring them into conformity with the new postulate.

The kind of adjustment made can be illustrated by stating that mathematical expressions of the following form appear frequently in the revised formulation of mechanics:

$$\sqrt{1-v^2/c^2}.$$

Here $v$ is a velocity – perhaps of one observer relative to another – and $c$ is the velocity of light. As we have already seen, $v/c$ is only about $1/10,000$ even when $v$ is the velocity of the earth in its orbital motion. The above-mentioned expression then has the value $0 \cdot 999999995$, which is only minutely different from unity. In ordinary laboratory experiments involving much smaller velocities the departure from unity would be even smaller. This explains why the laws of Newtonian mechanics had stood for so long without contradiction. For velocities small compared with the velocity of light the old laws remain valid, and indeed, all the new laws become indistinguishable from the old laws if only small velocities are considered. But for large velocities, such as the velocities of galaxies relative to each other, or those now attainable in particle accelerators, they lead to quite different conclusions.

It should not be imagined that it was an easy matter to set up the new laws. First, they had to represent correctly all relevant phenomena as known at the time. Furthermore, the greater complexity of the new mathematical structure meant that some of the basic concepts of mechanics had to be reconsidered. For example, it was necessary to reconsider the definitions of force, mass and acceleration and at this stage a certain freedom of choice was possible. In making a choice Einstein always favoured simplicity in mathematical form, and it is the great triumph of his genius that the theory of relativity as set out by him succeeded, not only in its immediate object of representing mechanical and electromagnetic behaviour as then known, but also in making a number of forecasts which have subsequently been verified by observation.

Without attempting an exact or full account, and without reference to whether the role of the theory was to provide clarification, explanation or prediction, we now mention briefly some of the main features of relativity theory.

(i) The concept of 'absolute time' has to be given up. Newton's view was that "Absolute, true, and mathematical time, of itself, and by its own nature, flows uniformly on, without regard to anything external". Now, however, it cannot be said that an event occurs at a given *absolute* time and accordingly absolute significance cannot be attached to simultaneity, nor can it necessarily be said for certain which of two events precedes the other if they occur at different places. It will depend on where the observer is situated relative to the locations of the two events, since the way in which he can receive the most exact information about their occurrence involves the passage of a light signal, travelling with finite velocity. If (in space) the observer is near event A, say, he might assert that it occurred before event B, whereas if he had been near event B he might have said the opposite.

(ii) In the same way, 'absolute space' is no longer a valid concept. For while one observer might say that two events occurred at the same place and at different times, another moving relative to him would say that the events occurred at different places. In a sense, space and time have clearly become linked by relativity, and this is why time is often spoken of (but without exact significance) as the 'fourth dimension'.

(iii) In the new mechanics it appears that the mass of a moving body is not the same as its mass at rest and that the gain in mass is $1/c^2$ times the kinetic energy due to the motion. Expressing it another way, the kinetic energy is $c^2$ times the gain in mass. Einstein's famous equation $E=mc^2$ represents the idea that the ordinary 'rest' mass of a body is also associated with an amount of energy equal to its mass multiplied by the square of the velocity of light. As we have seen in discussing nuclear phenomena, this is indeed an experimental fact.

(iv) Not only have the laws of mechanics, but Newton's law of gravitation also has to be modified. This was the problem dealt with by Einstein in the general theory of relativity which, as has been said, is concerned with observers who are travelling with accelerated motion relative to each other. Accelerated motion is, of course, characteristic of bodies moving under gravitational attraction. It was in this field that Einstein's most spectacular success was achieved, for he made three predictions which have been qualitatively verified by observation, even though the question of exact quantitative agreement has not yet been completely settled. He predicted that very slight differences from 'Newtonian' behaviour should be expected in the motions of the planets. Only Mercury is sufficiently near the sun to show a measurable difference, and the existence of a discrepancy was in fact already known to astronomers but not understood. Also, Einstein predicted correctly that light beams would be bent in a strong gravitational field (say, in passing close to the sun) and that spectral lines, which give information about the frequencies of atomic or molecular vibrations, would indicate an apparent slowing down of such processes on the sun. Some of these matters will be discussed further in later chapters.

The theory of relativity forms a popular background for discussions of a metaphysical nature because of some of its apparent absurdities. But in astronomy, and in the design of particle accelerators, it is simply a necessary part of the technique, because relativistic mechanics leads to a correct account of certain natural phenomena which could not otherwise be explained. Shorn of some of its overtones of fantasy, we see that the central principle of relativity is in effect no more than a restriction upon the type of theory which can have full validity in physics. Every theory must be verifiable in every laboratory, whatever its state of motion. Perhaps its main lesson for physicists is that they should keep open minds and should be prepared to question even their most firmly established ideas in the light of new discoveries. In particular, relativity suggests that one should beware of ideas like 'absolute time' independent of the observer.

*Quantum theory*

At about the same time as Einstein was carrying out his work on the behaviour of bodies of very large size or moving with very high velocities, classical physics was receiving another series of blows following some of the new discoveries in atomic physics. The first rift at this other end of the scale of natural phenomena had, however, come from an unexpected quarter when Planck proposed his quantum theory in 1900 as a result of his analysis of certain properties of thermal radiation. Subsequent developments went far beyond the scope of Planck's original theory and are distinguishable by different titles such as 'wave mechanics' and 'quantum mechanics'.

The problem studied by Planck was the distribution of energy among different wavelengths in the thermal radiation emitted by hot bodies. It had been shown earlier that there was a certain distribution of energy within any enclosure, and that this was in fact the same for all wavelengths at a given temperature, whatever the nature of the walls. It is easier to believe this assertion if it is realized that surfaces which are good emitters of radiation are also good absorbers, while bad emitters are bad absorbers, that is, good reflectors. So, although we might imagine that it takes longer to set up the required energy distribution in an enclosure with highly polished walls, this does not alter the final result. We can imagine the energy as being associated with radiation in the act of passing between the walls. Although the origin of the radiation must lie in the oscillations or vibrations of atoms (any oscillating dipole acts as a source of electromagnetic radiation), the fact that the amount of energy in the enclosure corresponding to a given wavelength did not depend on the walls suggested that the form of the distribution was in itself a fundamental fact of physics. The actual form is shown in Fig. 30 for two temperatures, 1,000° and 1,100°, on the absolute scale. It will be seen that at the higher temperature the peak in the curve is at shorter wavelength and beginning to overlap the region of visible light. The positions of the peaks of the distribution curves for various temperatures are indicated by the fine broken line.

We have not the space to explain to the reader precisely the theoretical situation as Planck found it. The theory included a discussion of the number of ways in which stationary waves of differing wavelengths could be set up in an enclosure rather similar to the discussion which led to the kinetic theory of gases. Let us merely say that the conclusion of the theory was that the curve of energy distribution against wavelength should show no peak but rise towards infinity at very short wavelengths. Planck's new postulate was that the energy of an oscillator (such as an

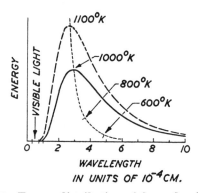

FIG. 30. *Energy distribution of thermal radiation.*

atom) could not vary continuously but could only take values which were multiples of the quantity $h\nu$, where $\nu$ is the frequency of the oscillation and $h$ a universal constant, which was the same for all types of oscillator. This is now known as Planck's constant. Further, he assumed that the emission or absorption of radiation was accompanied by a jump between two of these 'energy levels'. If the jump was downward, from higher to lower energy, radiation would be emitted. The absorption of radiation would lead to an upward jump.

Using these postulates Planck was able to modify the existing theory so as to account exactly for the form of the curves of Fig. 30. The complete success of the new theory caused much astonishment because of the revolutionary nature of the empirical assumptions made. For clearly the jump, or transition, between two adjacent energy levels could be accompanied only by an emission or absorption of the quantity, or 'quantum', of energy

$h\nu$. This suggested that radiation could be emitted in pulses, a concept which was out of harmony with the existing idea that light and other electromagnetic radiation were transmitted as continuous trains of waves. At the time this revolutionary concept had to stand, unsupported, as an *ad hoc* assumption leading to one specific and highly important result.

The next step was taken by Einstein who, a few months before the publication of his first paper on relativity, drew attention to the fact that other evidence existed for the suggestion that the exchange of energy between matter and electromagnetic radiation took place in pulses, or quanta of energy. This evidence came from the results of experiments on the photoelectric effect, which has been mentioned in Chapter I. It appeared quite unequivocally that the exchange of energy took place in quanta of energy $h\nu$, where $\nu$ is again the frequency of the incident light and $h$ is Planck's constant. At this stage, therefore, there was the confusing situation that although light appeared to have corpuscular properties, only by thinking of it as a wave, having wavelength and frequency, could one define the energy of the corpuscle, or 'photon'. And, of course, the body of knowledge about the wave-like properties of light remained valid.

The attribution of corpuscular properties to light was not, however, entirely unexpected because it was already known that light falling on any surface exerted a pressure, the so-called 'radiation pressure', upon it. This had been observed experimentally and is also a specific theoretical consequence in thermodynamics, electromagnetism and relativity theory.

### The Bohr atom

The next important development resulted from attempts to explain the characteristic spectra of certain substances. When a discharge in, say, hydrogen gas is examined in a spectroscope the resulting spectrum is not a continuous series of colours (the rainbow sequence) but consists of a number of bright lines at well-defined wavelengths – or colours – having obviously some systematic form of variation in their spacing. Now, although many regularities had previously been detected in the spectra of various elements, it was not until J. J. Balmer found, in 1885, that the wavelengths of the hydrogen lines could be represented by a simple empirical formula that the real challenge of this problem was fairly presented to the theoretician.

The starting-point of the theory was the idea that the emission of radiation was due to atomic 'oscillators'. The growing knowledge of the constitution of atoms suggested that these oscillators might be electrons in atoms revolving around the atomic nuclei, for a negative charge made to revolve around a positive charge would indeed emit radiation with frequency equal to the frequency of revolution. But a major difficulty presented itself immediately. For the loss of energy due to the emission of radiation would cause the electron to 'spiral' towards the nucleus at ever-increasing frequency of revolution. The emission of radiations of characteristic frequency, and, indeed, the continued existence of atoms, could hardly be explained on this basis.

The immediate solution of the difficulty was due to Bohr, who in 1913 made a number of radical postulates rather similar in type and content to those of Planck's original theory. He assumed that an electron could revolve around the nucleus at a fixed distance without radiating energy, and that there was a series of 'allowed orbits' in which this was possible. Only in the transition from one orbit to another could radiation be emitted or absorbed. In the case of a jump from an orbit to one nearer the nucleus there would be emission of radiation, while absorption of radiation could cause the corresponding outward jump. The frequency $\nu$ of the radiation was given by $\epsilon = h\nu$, where $\epsilon$ is here the difference between the energies of the two levels – usually known as 'quantum levels' or 'quantum states'. In the normal state of the atom the electron would occupy the orbit of lowest energy, but the absorption of radiation would raise it to a higher orbit; that is, the atom would be raised to an 'excited state'. Subsequently, radiation might be emitted by the fall from a higher orbit to a lower. At high temperatures many atoms can be excited by collisions with other atoms and then radiate energy by a fall into a lower state.

It is obvious in this case why an atom can absorb only radiations of frequency equal to those which it can emit, so that an emission spectrum is just like the 'negative' of an absorption spectrum. In fact, however, it is a universal property of all oscillators that they absorb well the frequencies which they emit well. A tuned violin string, for example, will vibrate sympathetically, or 'in resonance', if the correct note is sounded in the vicinity, and will therefore remove or absorb some of the energy in the sound wave.

By combining certain principles of classical mechanics and electrostatics with these new postulates, Niels Bohr was able to set up a mathematical theory which completely accounted for the main lines of the hydrogen spectrum. Later, other spectra were accounted for, and the question of the 'fine structure' of spectra – that is, of the 'splitting' of main spectral lines into groups of lines very close together – was dealt with successfully. It was shown, for example, that the variation of the mass of the electron with its velocity, as predicted by relativity, accounted for some of the fine structure. A good deal of supporting evidence about the existence of quantum states subsequently accumulated from other experiments.

*Wave mechanics*

Once again the adoption of postulates of a radical nature had brought order out of chaos. There remained, however, a certain feeling that these postulates had been too much of an *ad hoc* nature, and insufficiently related to other physical ideas. The next developments, though no less radical, provided such a completely satisfying synthesis of all the quantum phenomena that they removed the last doubts of physicists. These were the ideas of Louis de Broglie, Schrödinger, Dirac, Heisenberg and others, which find their most complete expression in modern 'wave mechanics'. The starting-point was a suggestion by de Broglie that, just as light had been found to have certain corpuscular properties, matter might have wave-like properties. A few years later this was shown to be true by Davisson and Germer in the U.S.A. and by G. P. Thomson, the son of J. J. Thomson, in Britain. They showed that a beam of electrons striking the surface of a crystal led to a pattern much in the same way as did a beam of X-rays. De Broglie assumed further that the frequency of the 'matter wave' associated with a particle could be found by use of the equation $\epsilon=h\nu$, which has already been mentioned, where $\epsilon$ is now the total energy (kinetic and potential) of the particle.

It is now seen that the reason why a simple 'particle' theory of the atom, using ordinary mechanics and electromagnetic theory, does not succeed is that the electron cannot be considered simply as a particle. It behaves in part as a wave also. Indeed, it is possible, by considering the de Broglie wavelength of a particle, to decide whether a 'classical' theory is likely to be adequate to account for its properties, or whether a theory along quantum lines will have to be developed. For a tennis ball moving with average velocity the de Broglie wavelength is minutely small in comparison with the size of the ball or of the tennis court. Classical mechanics will suffice in this case. For an electron moving over distances of the order of size of an oscilloscope or television tube the de Broglie wavelength is also much smaller than the length of path. But for an electron moving within an atom the distance is of the same order of size as the atom itself.

The full mathematical theory is far too complex and difficult to be discussed at any length here. It contains new ideas of an extraordinary character. For example, an idea of fundamental importance is that there is an ultimate uncertainty about the characteristics of any given particle which is not due to experimental or theoretical inadequacy; the particle cannot have both its position and velocity well-defined. If we imagine how we would try to determine experimentally, say, the exact position of an electron, this becomes evident. One approach would be to try to 'see' it. But this could not be done unless at least one photon had hit the electron, and it is known that this would give the electron a 'kick'. Theoretical physicists now believe generally that if something could not, even in principle, be measured or detected, it should not be regarded as significant.

The full theory, while somewhat altering the significance of Bohr's postulates, leads to a satisfying interpretation of them and gives a complete account of the hydrogen atom. The concept of orbits does not remain in quite the same form, but is still useful. The electronic 'shells' or 'sub-shells' which were mentioned in the last chapter correspond to certain groups of electronic orbits or quantum states, and in fact most of the emission and absorption of radiation corresponds to jumps between shells or sub-shells rather than within these groups.

Unfortunately, certain mathematical features of the theory make an extension to more complicated systems more and more difficult. It is hardly possible to make rigorous calculations about complicated systems and various methods of making reasonable approximations have been developed. The matter is very important in physics because it is believed that the technique of wave mechanics offers, in principle, the solution to most of the problems remaining in the field of atomic and molecular structure, inter-atomic forces and chemical behaviour, and the properties of matter in bulk. This is one of the main battle-grounds of the theoretical physicist today.

### Quantum theory of solids

There has been in recent years a spectacular development of a branch of physics known as 'solid state physics', as a result of the increasing understanding of quantum theory or wave mechanics. Many of the properties of matter, such as those which have been discussed in Chapter VI, can be accounted for fairly well without drawing too heavily on quantum ideas. This is because the de Broglie wavelength of an atom in a solid is rather small (though by no means negligible) in comparison with its size. But those properties which depend on the motions of electrons in solids have to be treated as quantum phenomena. The conduction of electricity in metals consists of motions of 'loose' electrons, and this has now received a very satisfactory treatment according to wave-mechanical theory. The 'fine structure' of solids forms an increasing part of the solid-state physicist's preoccupation because it is a feature of quantum theory that the whole of a lump of solid behaves as an atom (or molecule) in one respect: there is again a series of quantum levels – though now very closely spaced – which the electrons must occupy. It is the distribution of these quantum levels which ultimately determines the properties of a solid. Semi-conductors, those new materials which are becoming so important in transistors and other electronic devices, are materials which are intermediate between metals and non-metals. The task of the scientist here is to decide what distribution of quantum levels is required for a given purpose and then to try to achieve it in practice.

Very interesting results have been obtained in studies of the properties of solids at low temperatures. At first, low-temperature physics was concerned mainly with such questions as the condensation of gases such as oxygen, nitrogen, hydrogen and helium into the liquid and finally into the solid state. But it has now proved to be a most powerful approach to the study of the 'fine structure' of solids, in particular, of the distribution of quantum levels. Just as an atom at ordinary temperatures tends to be unexcited and to exist in the lowest quantum state, so the electrons in a piece of bulk matter, with much closer spacing of quantum levels, tend to fall into low quantum states at low temperatures. This gives rise to such phenomena as the spontaneous alignment of the electronic atomic 'magnets' if the temperature is lowered to about 1/100 degree above the absolute zero, and it is expected that below about 1/10,000 degree absolute the much weaker *nuclear* magnets will begin to align themselves. An unexpected discovery was that certain metals suddenly lose their resistance to the passage of electricity when cooled below characteristic temperatures. This property of 'superconductivity' is a challenge to both experimental and theoretical physicists, and is the subject of lively discussion among them.

Finally, the most spectacular of low-temperature effects, the properties of helium cooled below 2·1 degrees absolute, must be mentioned. Helium is unique in remaining liquid without solidification down to the lowest temperatures (though it can be solidified under pressure), and when it is cooled below this characteristic temperature its properties change in a remarkable way. It loses its viscosity and will 'siphon' itself into or out of vessels along a film, thick by atomic standards, which clings to every solid surface in its vicinity. The clue to much of this strange behaviour lies in the fact that the de Broglie wavelength of helium atoms at these temperatures is of the same order as their distance apart in the liquid. We might say loosely that the atoms are uncertain whether they are particles or waves! One consequence is that the volume of a given mass of liquid helium is much greater than would have been expected on 'classical' grounds.

*Philosophical implications of the discoveries of physics*

It is tempting to say simply that there are no philosophical implications to be attached to the matters which have been discussed here, but this would be to ignore the fact that violent controversies of a philosophical character have existed in physics at least since the time of Aristotle. At any rate, the tendency among physicists is now to consider that the real content of a statement in physics lies in the statement itself, and that to speak of its philosophical implication to some extent reduces the force of what is said. Let us try to illustrate this by some examples.

One of the most important scientific controversies was that between the followers of Aristotle and Ptolemy, who said that the sun and stars travelled around the earth, which was thus the centre of the universe, and the followers of Copernicus and Galileo, who insisted that the earth travelled around the sun. These opposite views would naturally be thought to have philosophical implications. Indeed, the Copernican hypothesis was attacked on religious grounds because it was asserted that Copernicus had removed an obstacle to the idea, opposed by the Church, that the universe might be infinite. It was unthinkable that stars travelling around the earth could move with infinite velocities, as some must in an infinite universe, if all revolved around the earth.

Now what Copernicus had found was that if he assumed the earth to be a planet, like the other planets, and that all moved around the sun, a great mathematical simplification occurred. He could then account for the seasons and for many other features of the planetary motion. So he asserted that the earth moved around the sun. This idea was at the time a great scientific advance. But with our present knowledge of astronomy we know also that the sun is moving around the centre of the stellar system; when an astronomer studies distant nebulae the situation is still further complicated. So how is the earth really moving? Surely the real truth is that which is contained in the sum of all detailed assertions about relative motions. For practical purposes any suitable hypothesis may be used: a cyclist who wished to know what was lighting-up time would find the Ptolemaic system adequate.

This old controversy carries its lesson even today. Anyone

brought up in the Aristotelian tradition would resist strongly any suggestion that the earth was rotating on its own axis and re- volving around the sun at enormous speed. All the evidence of the senses would persuade him that this must be a fantastic in- vention. Eventually, after calmer reflection, he would realize that it was really a very reasonable idea because it explained all the complex planetary motions – relative to the earth – as being also quite simple revolutions around the sun. Finally, he might arrive at the more empirical view, suggested above, that the real truth was the sum of knowledge about relative motions.

Nowadays, the ideas of relativity and quantum theory appear strange. But when they have been thoroughly assimilated future students of present-day writings on their philosophical implica- tions may wonder what all the fuss was about! If a theory leads to a simplification or greater ordering of ideas then it is useful. The physicist does not argue as to whether it is *right*. In par- ticular, he does not worry if he cannot explain the new postulates made. We have deceived ourselves if we think that anything can be *explained* – in the mystical, absolute sense usually attached to this word. It is only because of our extreme familiarity, almost from birth, with some of the ideas of classical physics that modern physics is so puzzling. For example, the indestructibility of matter seems so obvious from all our experience that the state- ment that matter can be converted into energy is difficult to accept. Also, we have rather firm ideas about the meanings of such words as 'force' and 'cause', because we know how to exert forces (with our muscles, say) and we can also cause events to occur. It is disturbing to be told that force has to be redefined in order to carry through the development of relativity theory, or that force can be transmitted without the intervention of a medium, or that certain physical events appear to occur without cause – a feature of quantum theory.

It becomes less difficult to accept such changes when it is realized that the concept of force is in itself empirical and some- what synthetic. When Newton's second law is objectively ana- lysed we come to realize that what it does is to define force only if mass and acceleration have previously been defined. In rela- tivity the definition of force is slightly altered and the question naturally arises as to whether such a thing as *force* really exists. The answer is that force is what we have now decided it shall be, and we have chosen the present definition because it leads to an *all-round* simplification of the laws of nature in their mathematical formulation. That is, force, as now defined, enters simply into many other physical laws besides Newton's second law.

It is useful when considering any statement about the philosophical implications of science to apply two tests. First: is the statement framed with the same care as scientific statements usually are; do the words used convey a precise meaning, and the same meaning to everyone concerned in the discussion? At this point it is only being insisted that the same rigour in argument be employed as is required by modern philosophers – who have, as a matter of fact, been as fundamentally influenced by the objectivity and empiricism of science as by the exact reasoning of modern mathematics. But very many of the assertions which have been made about the philosophical implications of science would fall to the ground when analysed in this way. Secondly: is that which is implied really contained in that established by the scientific experiment? This requirement seems so obvious that it is surprising to find how many philosophical assertions are made which fail to meet it. For example, it is often said that because of the element of uncertainty introduced into quantum theory by wave mechanics there is an ultimate limit to human knowledge. Even this statement can be challenged, but it will often be added that it implies that man is an imperfect creature who should not presume to probe too deeply into scientific problems. Or it may be said that, because the concept of causality seems to disappear in certain quantum phenomena, man does have the power of making his own decisions. These arguments will hardly bear examination. At the very least it should be emphasized that the first part of each assertion is about electrons or nucleons; the second part is about man.

The scientific attitude is to avoid assertions containing terms which have not been objectively defined, and to regard each assertion about scientific fact as meaning precisely what it means and as containing precisely what it contains, neither more nor less.

F

# CHAPTER VIII

# The solar system

## The solar constant

For us living on the earth the most important other single large body in the universe is the sun. The sun is our main source of light, heat and energy. Of course, there are some energy sources on the earth, such as earthquakes, volcanoes, hot springs and lunar tides, that do not come from the sun. Nor is nuclear energy due to solar action. But the main energy sources which we use at present in everyday life, like gas and electricity, are obtained from coal, oil and water-power; the energy in coal and oil is ultimately derived from solar energy trapped by plants in the far distant past, and that in water-power is due to solar energy which raises vapour from the seas and oceans. These sources, as well as winds and solar tides, all bring energy to us which can ultimately be traced to the action of the sun on terrestrial matter.

What then is the sun? It can be regarded as a machine which generates its own energy as it radiates. As far as we on earth are concerned, its most important feature is its regularity of behaviour. Not only does the sun radiate energy at a steady rate, but it also holds the earth at a more or less constant distance. We tend to take all this for granted, for, as an American astronomer has remarked, the sun is like a dependable and steady husband who is rarely fully appreciated! If the sun's action on the earth were not so remarkably steady, there is no doubt that life would soon perish from the earth.

The steadiness of the sun's supply of energy to the earth is expressed in terms of what is known as the 'solar constant'. This is defined as the amount of heat in calories which would fall in one minute on an area one square centimetre placed perpendicular to the radiation as it falls on the earth's surface, if the earth had no atmosphere and were at its mean distance from the sun. Consequently, to determine the solar constant, the actual amount of energy which falls per square centimetre per minute must be measured and then the result must be corrected for the absorption by the earth's atmosphere. The final figure is nearly two calories per square centimetre per minute.

From the ages of fossil-bearing rocks which have been determined by means of radioactive measurements, we deduce that life has existed on the earth for upwards of 500 million years. During all this time the solar constant cannot have changed greatly, because if it had become either twice as large or half as large as it is now, then, in either case, all life would certainly have perished. Consequently, both the solar distance and the sun's rate of generation of radiation must have varied comparatively little over this vast span of time, which, on some theories at least, may be about 10 per cent of the age of the whole universe.

### The sun's distance

The sun's distance from us, although on the whole very nearly constant, oscillates a little. Its average value is taken as the fundamental distance in astronomy and is known as the astronomical unit. There are several methods by which it may be estimated. For example, it may be determined by means of the solar parallax, which is the angle subtended by the radius of the earth at the centre of the sun; knowing the radius of the earth, we can then calculate the distance. In practice, the solar parallax is obtained by considering the position of the sun relative to the background of the stars from two widely separated observatories on the earth's surface. Knowing the base-line between these observatories and measuring the relevant angles, the solar parallax, and hence the sun's distance, can be determined geometrically. The result thus obtained can be checked as there are other methods by which this fundamental unit may be estimated.

Indeed, the sun's distance from the earth can be calculated indirectly by determining the distance of any one planet. This is a consequence of the remarkable fact that, without measuring any celestial distance whatsoever, we can draw a scale-map of the solar system, although of course we do not know, without measuring some distance, what the scale is. This can be done in more than one way. The most important method depends upon Kepler's law of planetary motion, that, to a first approximation, the squares of the periods of revolution of the planets around the sun are proportional to the cubes of their mean distances from the sun. From the angular motions of the planets their periods can be obtained and the ratios of their mean distances determined. But one distance, say the distance of a particular planet from the earth or from the sun, must be measured in order to determine the scale and hence the actual distances.

The most recent determinations of this kind were based on observations of one of the minor planets, Eros, which, in 1931, came within 16,000,000 miles of the earth, which is a small distance for celestial objects. As a result of many years work on these observations, in which the leading part was taken by Sir Harold Spencer Jones, the mean distance of the sun was ultimately determined to be 93,009,000 miles.

The sun's distance, however, is not absolutely constant. This can immediately be deduced from the fact that the sun's diameter does not always subtend the same angle at the earth. During the course of the year, this angle varies by more than one minute of arc. Although the seasons are not primarily determined by this variation in distance, but by the fact that the earth's axis of daily rotation is not exactly perpendicular to the earth's orbit, it has an important secondary effect. In December the sun is only about 91,000,000 miles away and in June about 94,000,000 miles; consequently there are greater extremes of climate in the southern hemisphere.

### The rate of energy generation by the sun

Knowing the sun's distance, it is possible to calculate the size of the sun and hence, given the solar constant, the rate of emission of energy per unit of surface area. Its diameter is found to be about 864,000 miles, or about 109 times the diameter of the earth. Each square centimetre of the solar surface radiates, on the average, about 90,000 calories a minute, *i.e.* at the rate of a 9 horse-power engine. The earth receives rather less than one part in 200 million of the total energy radiated by the sun, but even this small fraction is something like 5 million horse-power per square mile.

We have here an immense potential source of energy which has not yet been effectively utilized.

In the course of the year the total output of heat from the sun amounts to $3 \times 10^{33}$ calories. This seems an enormous quantity, but to appreciate its significance we must relate it to the mass of, or amount of matter in, the sun. This can be determined by appeal to the Newtonian theory of gravitation. Knowing the radius of the earth, the gravitational acceleration on the earth's surface, the distance of the sun and the acceleration of the earth in its orbital motion, we can compare the mass of the sun with the mass of the earth: the sun is about 332,000 times as massive. To obtain the mass of the earth, the constant of gravitation which controls the strength of gravitational fields must be determined experimentally. An accurate value was obtained more than half a century ago – a fairly good estimate had already been obtained in the 18th century by Cavendish – from which it was deduced that the mass of the earth is about $6 \times 10^{27}$ grams. Consequently, the mass of the sun is about $2 \times 10^{33}$ grams.

Comparing this figure with the sun's energy output per year of about $3 \times 10^{33}$ calories, we see that to each 2 grams of the sun's mass there is a generation of energy of 3 calories per year. This does not seem very remarkable at first sight, but it becomes utterly fantastic when we take into account the enormous time for which it has continued. From the evidence of past life on the earth, it is clear that this steady generation of energy must have been going on for upwards of 500 million years and probably for considerably longer. Thus, during 500 million years or more, nearly 1,000 million calories have been generated *per gram* of the sun's mass at a more or less steady rate. This is a truly stupendous figure. It has been calculated that 1 gram of the ideal mixture of coal and oxygen for complete combustion could generate about 2,000 calories, so that, if the sun were composed of such an ideal mixture of coal and oxygen, the whole of the sun's mass would have been burned up in rather less than two thousand years. Thus, chemical combustion is obviously not the method by which the sun generates energy.

During the latter part of the 19th century a great deal of attention was paid to this problem. It was one of the great puzzles of physical science at that time. The German physicist Helmholtz looked for some other source of energy generation and came to the conclusion that the only source which could endure for such a long period was gravitational contraction. He pointed out that, if the sun slowly contracted under its own gravitation, there would be a loss of gravitational energy which might be a source of radiant energy. To generate sufficient energy the sun's radius would have to contract at the rate of 75 metres per year at the present time. If we calculate backwards to get a steady rate of energy generation all the time, we find that the rate of contraction would have been faster in the past. Extrapolating to a state when the sun was a very tenuous nebula, the longest period that can be obtained is approximately 20 million years. Helmholtz thought that this was roughly the age of the sun, but he and his followers were involved in a notorious controversy with geologists who rejected this period as utterly inadequate, although at that time they had no precise means of dating fossils. The controversy was only resolved this century with the aid of nuclear physics. Before going into this problem further, two other questions must be considered: first, the sun's temperature, and second, the sun's chemical composition.

## The temperature and chemical composition of the sun

Knowing the solar constant, it is comparatively easy to estimate the surface temperature of the sun. We can appeal to different physical laws characterizing so-called black-body radiation (a black-body is a perfect radiator – see, for example, Fig. 30). According to which law is invoked, temperatures of 5,500° and 5,900°C., respectively, are obtained. The fact that these two are not exactly the same shows that the sun is not quite a perfect radiator, but the agreement is sufficiently good to show that the sun's effective surface temperature must be in this region. These figures may be compared with the temperature of an ordinary electric arc which is about 4,000°C. They may sound large by our standards, but are very modest for celestial temperatures. Theories of stellar structure enable estimates to be made for the temperature at the centre of the sun. It is generally accepted today that this temperature must be of the order of 20,000,000°C.

The second question that must be considered is the composition of the sun. A hundred or so years ago, the famous French positivist philosopher Auguste Comte stated dogmatically that we shall never know of what the stars are made. He was answered not long afterwards by the rise of the science of astronomical spectroscopy, by means of which the chemical composition of any incandescent celestial body can be analysed provided a sufficiently detailed spectrum is obtained. The sun's spectrum is found to be enormously complex; it is a continuous spectrum crossed by a large number of dark lines called absorption lines. The continuous spectrum is produced by the photosphere, or surface of the main body of the sun. Above this is the lower part of the solar atmosphere, known as the reversing layer, which, being at a somewhat lower temperature, absorbs from the continuous spectrum below the particular colours, or spectral lines, which it would otherwise emit. Normally, the spectrum of an incandescent gas is an emission spectrum consisting of bright lines depending on the chemical composition. In the case of the sun roughly 20,000 absorption lines have been observed and more than half of them have been identified.

Broadly speaking, the same elements exist in the sun as here on earth. For various reasons some elements found on earth are not directly observed in the sun and in one remarkable instance an element was first detected in the sun by Lockyer in 1868 before it was discovered in the laboratory by Ramsay in 1895. This element was appropriately named helium.

To find the particular method by which the sun generates energy, it is essential to know, not merely the actual elements that occur in the sun, but their relative abundances. These can be deduced by studying the forms and strengths of lines in the solar spectrum. Although the proportions of metals, such as iron, nickel and calcium, are roughly the same on the earth and the sun, there is an important difference: the sun's atmosphere consists mainly of hydrogen, and to a much lesser extent of helium. This difference is not due to a peculiarity of the sun's composition, but of the earth's, for throughout the universe hydrogen is by far the most abundant element. It is thought to characterize the sun as a whole, not merely its atmosphere. This conclusion is the key to the solution of the problem of solar energy generation.

*The method of energy generation by the sun*

According to Einstein's mass-energy relation, there is bottled up in each gram of matter about 20 million million calories of rest-mass energy. The sun's radiation, which has been going on for upwards of 500 million years, has required the generation of nearly 1,000 million calories per gram. If this figure is compared with the 20 million million calories locked up in each gram of matter, it is clear that only one part in 20,000 of the total inertial energy of the sun need be drawn upon. Even if the sun has gone on radiating much longer than 500 million years, this source would be more than ample.

How can this source be tapped? As already explained in Chapter IV, two possible processes are now envisaged, both of which require very high temperatures for their operation. They both involve the transmutation of hydrogen into helium. It will be remembered that the release of energy in this transmutation depends on the fact that, although the nucleus of the helium atom can be formed from the nuclei of four hydrogen atoms, the mass of the helium nucleus is actually slightly less than that of the four original hydrogen nuclei, the loss being about 0·8 per cent. This means that for every gram of hydrogen the resulting loss of mass is equivalent to the release of roughly 160 thousand million calories.

Of the two processes, the one known as the hydrogen chain is believed to be the predominant reaction in the sun, while in larger stars the carbon cycle is thought to be the chief source of energy. We have seen that, in order to maintain a steady supply of radiation in a period of 500 million years, the sun need have drawn on only about one part in 20,000 of its available inertial energy, and in 1,000 million years it need have consumed the equivalent of only one part in 10,000 of its mass. Since the loss of mass when hydrogen is converted into helium is about 1 per cent, only about 1 or 2 per cent of the sun's hydrogen need have been converted into helium in the past 1,000 million years. Consequently, over this vast range of time the net change in the sun's composition and constitution has been sufficiently small to account for the presumed regularity in its rate of radiation, thus showing that the theory is self-consistent.

The tremendous scale on which the solar furnace operates is evident from the fact that some 800 million tons of hydrogen are converted into helium every second. This results in a loss of mass exceeding 6 million tons a second which is converted into energy. It has been estimated that the sun can go on steadily burning up its hydrogen at this rate for another 50,000 million years, but in all probability the sun cannot consume in this way more than a fraction of its supply of hydrogen. In this case, the process may continue for only 5,000–10,000 million years.

How does the heat produced inside the sun escape to the surface and so ultimately pass across the intervening space to us? It might be conveyed from the interior to the surface by conduction, convection or radiation. Despite the enormous pressures which must prevail inside the sun, the sun is believed to be gaseous throughout. Consequently, heat must be conveyed mainly by convection or radiation. Near the surface the solar prominences provide dramatic evidence of vertical mixing. Nevertheless, despite this evidence of convection, it is believed that radiation is responsible for most of the energy-transport from the interior of the sun outwards.

*Solar activity*

Detailed study of the surface of the sun is facilitated by an instrument known as the spectroheliograph. The solar image is permitted to drift across the slit of a spectrograph, so that with the aid of a second slit at the focus the light passes to a photographic plate. In this way a monochromatic picture of the whole disc of the sun is obtained, that is a picture of the whole disc taken in one wavelength of light. This looks quite different from the sun as normally seen in light of all wavelengths simultaneously. Remarkable details are revealed, particularly if these monochromatic pictures are taken in the wavelengths of the most prominent lines on the sun's spectrum, pointing to the great turbulence of the solar atmosphere (see Plate XV).

The best-known markings on the sun's disc are the great sunspots which were first realized to be solar by Galileo when, in 1610, he applied the telescope to astronomical observation. As a result of this discovery it was found that the sun rotates, for although the spots are not absolutely fixed on the sun's surface they can be used statistically to estimate the sun's rotation. This rotation is very different from that of the earth, which is the same everywhere. In the case of the sun, rotation varies according to latitude: near the solar equator the period is about 24½ days, whereas near the poles it is about 34 days. The cause of this variation is unknown, but it shows that there must be continual mixing of material on the solar surface.

Although the spots show up as dark, they are not actually cold but are merely some 2,000°C. cooler than their surroundings. Sunspots often occur in groups with two leading members. Near the spots there are frequently bright patches known as *faculae*, meaning 'little torches' (from the Latin). These faculae often endure much longer than the spots themselves. They are thought to be temporary mountains of hot gas rising above the solar surface. The cause of the spots still remains a mystery.

One of the principal discoveries about sunspots was made by G. E. Hale at Mount Wilson in California. It was known that a magnetic field gives rise to a characteristic splitting of spectral lines. Hale found such an effect in sunspot spectra and concluded that sunspots have strong magnetic fields. Pairs of spots usually have opposite magnetic polarity. Records show that the numbers of spots visible each day oscillate more or less rhythmically in a cycle with a mean period of rather more than eleven years.

### The corona

At the time of a solar eclipse there comes into view one of the most beautiful sights in the skies, the pearly halo around the sun known as the corona. Shortly before the last war the French astronomer B. Lyot invented an instrument known as the coronograph, by means of which the corona can be studied at any time and not only when there is a total solar eclipse; this instrument in effect produces an artificial eclipse. Although Lyot's coronograph does not show all the details which are observable during a total eclipse, it can be used continually in order to study the sequence of changes of the corona. Moreover, with its aid cinematograph records can be obtained.

The structure of the corona is complex. It varies with the sunspot cycle: at sunspot maximum it is compact, whereas at sunspot minimum there are short streamers which, it has been suggested, may indicate the positions of the sun's magnetic poles. At present, however, there is some doubt whether the sun really does possess a general magnetic field. Sometimes long streamers are also seen emanating from the corona.

Superimposed on the spectrum of the corona are a number of bright emission lines which for long remained a puzzle to astrophysicists as they did not seem to be related to any known chemical element. Indeed at one time an artificial element, known as 'coronium', was invented to account for them. But as the science of chemistry and physics developed, the Periodic Table (Fig. 3) was gradually filled up and there seemed to be no place in it for this mysterious element. Astrophysicists came to the conclusion that these emission lines must be due to familiar substances distorted in some way by the curious physical conditions which it was presumed must prevail in the corona. Finally, in 1940, B. Edlén, a Swedish spectroscopist, put forward what is now thought to be the correct explanation, that these peculiar lines are due to highly ionized atoms which have lost a large number of their attendant electrons. By a brilliant combination of theory and experiment he showed that many of these lines are due to atoms of iron which have lost 9, 10, 12 or even 13 electrons. Neutral iron has 26 attendant electrons per atom, whereas the most prominent green line in the coronal spectrum is due to iron which has lost 50 per cent of its satellite electrons. Such a drastic stripping of electrons from atoms occurs at high temperatures, and the surprising conclusion of Edlén's investigation was that extraordinarily high temperatures must prevail in the corona. This result has been confirmed by the observation of the broadening of the spectral lines, which is again a typical consequence of high temperatures. For the observed stripping of 13 electrons from iron, temperatures higher than 1,000,000°C. are required.

*Solar-terrestrial relationships*

We not only receive heat and light from the sun but also material particles. This was first discovered by studying variations in the earth's magnetism known as magnetic storms. As long ago as 1859 Carrington at Greenwich found that certain bright flares on the sun were followed on the two following days by fluctuations in the strength of the earth's magnetic field. Just over twenty years ago Sydney Chapman and V. C. A. Ferraro put forward their well-known theory that in such a flare streams of protons and electrons, in more or less equal numbers and hence electrically neutral, are ejected from the sun. If a stream is directed towards the earth, it may impinge on the earth's atmosphere a day or more later.

It has been suggested that these particles are deflected mainly towards the magnetic poles and give rise in extreme northern and southern latitudes to the spectacle of the Aurora Borealis. Also these particles generate powerful electric currents which tend to produce the magnetic storms mentioned earlier. The theory is supported, first by the observation of lines of neutral hydrogen in the auroral spectra, indicating the presence of equal numbers of protons and electrons, and secondly by the displacement of these lines in a manner which is consistent with the motion assigned to the particles concerned. The long white streamers which are sometimes seen in the corona may also be corpuscular streams.

It has long been suspected that there is not only a relation between these terrestrial effects and solar flares, but also with sunspots. If such a relation exists, then it must be complex and somewhat elusive, because the presence of a large spot is not necessarily an indication that there will be a violent magnetic storm, and conversely such a storm can occur when there are no large spots on the sun.

*The sun's gravitational field*

Since the Copernican theory came to be generally accepted, the other important invariable feature of the sun, its constancy of apparent motion, has been regarded as due to the constancy of the earth's motion about the sun under the influence of the sun's gravitational field. Given the earth's mean distance from the sun, the strength of the sun's gravitational field determines the length of the year.

The sun's superficial gravity is nearly 28 times that of the earth; so that a quartern loaf, if one could imagine it transported to the sun's surface without being affected by the heat, would weigh nearly a hundredweight, whereas if it were carried to the moon it would weigh less than three-quarters of a pound. The primary effect of the sun's gravitational field is to hold the solar system together. This was first made clear by Newton who followed Copernicus in regarding the sun as the central body. Decisive observational support for the Copernican theory was obtained by Galileo in 1610 when he first turned his telescope to the observation of the planets.

### Venus and Jupiter

The two planets which Galileo found to be most useful for confirming the Copernican theory were Venus and Jupiter. According to the Ptolemaic theory, Venus moved about the sun in such a way that always less than half of its surface appeared to be illuminated. The phases of Venus cannot be observed by the naked eye, but with his telescope Galileo discovered that, although Venus has phases, it is sometimes gibbous in appearance. This was a strong argument against the Ptolemaic theory.

Of even greater importance was Galileo's discovery of the four major satellites of Jupiter. One of the most powerful arguments that had been brought to bear against the Copernican theory was that, if all the other bodies in the solar system were to move around the sun, why should the moon be the only exception and move around the earth? Why did the other planets not have moons, too? Galileo wrote of his discovery, "Jupiter removes the apparent anomaly of the Copernican system, that the earth was the only planet with a moon going round it." Since 1892 other satellites of Jupiter have been discovered. They are very much smaller than the four Galilean ones, which are all of comparable size with our own moon. At times Jupiter's satellites can be seen casting shadows on Jupiter (see Plate XVI).

Jupiter's Galilean satellites again played a major role in the history of knowledge some sixty-five years later. In 1675 the Danish astronomer O. Roemer observed a curious discrepancy in the times of the eclipses of the satellites of Jupiter. Sometimes the eclipses occurred earlier than predicted and sometimes later. Roemer interpreted these discrepancies as being due to the fact that light is not propagated instantaneously but travels with a finite speed. The time at which the eclipse of a Jovian satellite is observed will depend on the distance of the earth from Jupiter, and this distance may vary by as much as the diameter of the earth's orbit about the sun. Roemer estimated that the maximum difference would be 22 minutes, whereas modern observations make it about $16\frac{1}{2}$ minutes. These figures relate to the time that light takes to travel a distance equal to the diameter of the earth's orbit about the sun. Hence, given the diameter of the earth's orbit, the velocity of light can be calculated. Despite its inaccuracy, Roemer's achievement was a remarkable one: for the first time in the history of science it was shown not only that light travels with a finite speed but moreover what the order of magnitude of that speed was. The correct value is nearly 300,000 kilometres, or 186,000 miles, per second.

*Saturn*

Jupiter with its numerous moons forms a solar system in miniature. So, too, does Saturn with its satellites, but its ring system is unique. The first person to see the rings was Galileo, although his telescope was not adequate to reveal their shape. It was Huygens who first succeeded, in 1655, in perceiving the ring form. Twenty years later Cassini resolved it into two concentric rings with a narrow dark division between them (see Plate XVII).

The rings are remarkably flat and thin and when presented to us edge-on we do not see them at all. They are not continuous solid or liquid structures, but consist of a swarm of discrete particles of matter each describing its own orbit about Saturn. It was shown by Clerk Maxwell in 1857 that continuous solid or liquid rings would be unstable and would break up under the tidal influence of Saturn. Only a swarm of separate bodies moving in nearly circular orbits in one plane could form a stable system. There is much observational evidence in support of this theory.

The rings have been found to be excellent reflectors of light, and it is known that matter generally reflects better when pulverized. The constituent particles are probably quite small, like ordinary dust, but not so small as to be forced away from Saturn by pressure of the light which Saturn reflects from the sun. The American astronomer Kuiper has suggested that, as the particles have good reflecting surfaces, they are either composed of ice or else are covered with frost.

Saturn has nine satellites of which one, Titan, is remarkable in being the only satellite in the solar system with a detectable atmosphere. Kuiper believes that the atmosphere of Saturn originally extended beyond Titan which, owing to its compara- tively large mass (nearly twice that of the moon), succeeded in retaining some of this atmosphere, and that the five minor satellites and the ring system were formed within this atmosphere as it cooled. The ring system may have been due to the disruption of a satellite which came too near to Saturn and was broken up by tide-raising forces into a number of small particles which finally settled down into a ring under gravitational action. The ring has actually three divisions, one being much more prominent than the other two. They are thought to be regions of instability for the motions of particles, whereas the bright parts are regions where particles can move in stable orbits around Saturn.

## Planetary atmospheres

The theory of the existence and chemical composition of the atmospheres of celestial bodies is based on the concept of velocity of escape. The velocity of escape at the surface of a body is that velocity with which a particle must be projected if it is to leave the body and never return to it despite the influence of gravity. At the sun's surface this velocity is about 55 times as great as the corresponding velocity on the surface of the earth. If a rocket is to leave the earth for outer space, it must be projected with a speed in excess of 11·3 kilometres, or about 7 miles, a second. To leave the sun it would have to be ejected with a speed greater than 622 kilometres a second, whereas on the moon it need only be projected with a speed greater than 2·4 kilometres a second.

For a particular gas to be retained for many millions of years in the atmosphere of a planet, or other body, it has been calculated that the *average* velocity of its constituent molecules must not exceed about *one fifth* of the velocity of escape. Otherwise, as a result of continual collisions, almost all the molecules will in time acquire the velocity of escape when near the boundary of the atmosphere and be dissipated into outer space. The average velocity of the molecules varies from gas to gas and also depends upon temperature. As already mentioned, the higher the temperature, the greater the average velocity.

Therefore, a planet near the sun, like Mercury, will have a worse chance than a planet farther away of retaining any particular gas, because Mercury is exposed to a much higher temperature from the sun's radiation. Also Mercury is a comparatively small planet and consequently has a weaker gravitational field. Calculations on these lines suggest that neither Mercury nor the moon should have any atmosphere, results that are confirmed by observation. On the other hand, Venus, Mars, Jupiter, Saturn, Uranus and Neptune all have atmospheres.

The surface temperatures of Jupiter and Saturn are much lower than those prevailing on the earth, an average of −120°C. on Jupiter and −140°C. on Saturn, those on Uranus and Neptune being even lower. The molecular velocities are correspondingly lower and, moreover, the gravitational fields are stronger. Hence, unpleasant gases like methane and ammonia are retained in the atmospheres of these bodies. Venus, on the other hand, is thought to retain in its atmosphere gases similar to those on the earth, but it seems to be covered with cloud which probably contains much water vapour. Conditions on the surface are believed to be governed by the greenhouse effect: a considerable part of the solar heat which falls on Venus is trapped beneath the clouds. Thus, although there is probably much water on the surface of Venus, it must all be very nearly at boiling-point.

The most favourable extra-terrestrial place in the solar system to seek for atmospheric conditions which might be consistent with the existence of life is Mars. One of the most convincing arguments for assuming that Mars has an atmosphere is its appearance when photographed in the red and in the blue. As shown on Plate XVIII, Mars appears larger in blue light than in red, the reason being that planetary atmospheres, like that of the earth, tend to scatter sunlight in the blue. Comparison of the photographic plates leads to the conclusion that the depth of the Martian atmosphere must be about sixty miles. Although there is some uncertainty concerning its composition, the density at its base is believed to be comparable with that at the top of Mount Everest, where nothing can live under natural conditions. Hence, it seems unlikely that there is much life on Mars, except possibly some very primitive vegetation. Recently, when studying the spectra of the planets with the aid of photo-electric cells of high sensitivity in the infra-red, Kuiper found that the greenish areas on Mars show no trace of the infra-red spectrum of chlorophyll, the green colouring matter in terrestrial vegetation.

## The debris of the solar system

There are many other constituents of the solar system besides planets and satellites, for example, minor planets, comets, meteors and meteorites. Together they all bear witness to the existence of a certain amount of diffuse material within the system. The fact that tails of comets tend to be directed away from the sun is evidence that these tails are formed by large numbers of small-sized particles streaming away from the head under the influence of the sun's radiation pressure, which must exceed the sun's gravitational attraction. Only if the particles concerned are rather bigger than molecules and approach the size of very small particles of dust will this occur.

There is some indirect evidence for the hypothesis that there was much more diffuse interplanetary matter – gas and dust – scattered throughout the solar system in the distant past than there is today. Except for the extreme cases of Mercury and Pluto (the planet most distant from the sun), the eccentricities of the orbits of the planets are so small that they differ very little from circles. It is known from theory that if at one time there existed a cloud of diffuse material throughout the system, then resistance to motion would have had the effect of progressively diminishing the eccentricities of the planetary orbits, which would gradually have become more and more circular. Since there is no reason why the primaeval orbits should have been very nearly circular, it is thought that there must once have been much more diffuse interplanetary material than there is today.

### The origin of the solar system

There is still no agreed theory on how the solar system originally came into being, and it may well be that none will ever be generally accepted. Some theories are based on the assumption that very peculiar conditions were required to originate such a system, but as these conditions must have existed a very long time ago, there may be no comparable situation today by which these theories could be directly tested.

About a century and half ago Laplace put forward his famous nebular hypothesis, according to which the solar system originated in a vast diffuse rotating mass. As this condensed under its own gravitational action, rings split off and condensed into planets. Although this hypothesis fell out of favour for a time, it has recently been revived in a modified form.

Meanwhile many other hypotheses have been put forward. According to one, the sun passed at some time very near another star which drew out material from it and this filament ultimately condensed into separate planets. The very close approach of two stars which were formerly far apart must, however, be a very rare event. Nevertheless, the main objection to this hypothesis is its failure to account for the peculiar distribution of rotational, or angular, momentum in the solar system, which is mainly carried by outer planets of far less mass than the sun.

Another hypothesis is based on the assumption that the sun was originally a member of a binary system. The other star, having suffered a direct collision with a third star, broke up and the planets were formed from the resulting fragments. However, in view of the high temperatures that might be expected to arise, it is more probable that the material would just stream out into space than condense into planets.

A Swedish physicist, H. Alfvén, has drawn attention to the possibility that forces other than gravitational may have played a significant role in the genesis of the solar system. He has developed a theory in which magnetic forces play an important part. Unfortunately, there is no evidence that such forces ever existed on the scale required. Moreover, as already mentioned, recent observational evidence has led to the conclusion that, contrary to what used to be thought, the sun may have no appreciable general magnetic field.

Two much more plausible theories recently put forward by C. F. von Weizsaecker and H. C. Urey, respectively, are similar to Laplace's theory. According to von Weizsaecker, the sun passing through an interstellar cloud of diffuse material captured part of it. Numerous eddies formed in this cloud. which became very turbulent. From a detailed consideration of the vortices that might occur, von Weizsaecker has shown how the planets and satellites could have been generated.

Whereas in von Weizsaecker's theory the solar system began when the sun was already a hot star, in Urey's the whole system began at a low temperature. The sun was created at the same time as the rest of the solar system from some kind of cloud in which condensations occurred, the largest giving rise to the sun and the others to the planets and satellites. The largest condensation, being so much more massive than the others, eventually became a star and raised the temperatures of the smaller bodies in the space surrounding it. However, their surface temperatures never rose to more than about 2,000°C. and afterwards fell to their present values. The conditions which prevail within this range of temperatures give rise to much more complex phenomena than those associated with the high temperatures of the sun and stars. The study of these phenomena is primarily the concern of the chemist, and Urey's approach to cosmogony is unique in being that of the chemist rather than that of the mathematicians and physicists who alone had studied the subject before.

Throughout the universe there are millions of stars like the sun and many astronomers believe that there must be many other planetary systems. Despite the spectacular advances in observational technique in the present century, however, no conclusive observational evidence of any other such system has yet been obtained. For all we know at present, the solar system may be unique. And it may well be that we shall never know whether there exists a world similar to ours elsewhere.

Great as are the distances between the sun and the planets, they are minute compared with the vast distances of interstellar space. Light from the sun takes about eight minutes to reach us on the earth. It can span the distance right out to Pluto on the apparent confines of the solar system in about five and a half hours, but light from the nearest known star, Proxima Centauri, takes more than four years to reach us.

# CHAPTER IX

# The Milky Way

## Wright, Kant and Herschel

Until the latter part of the 18th century the principal object of astronomical investigation was the solar system. The stars were regarded as forming a mere framework of reference against which the motions of the planets and other bodies in the solar system could be studied and measured. Copernicus, Kepler and Galileo, by transferring the origin of reference from the earth to the sun, have been regarded as responsible for one of the greatest revolutions in the history of man's ideas concerning the universe and his relation to the universe. Nevertheless, despite its shattering impact on human thought, the Copernican revolution was merely a rearrangement of the same pieces on the same chessboard, whereas the astronomical revolution of the second half of the 18th century substituted an entirely new chessboard for the old one and an entirely new set of pieces. The background now came into the foreground of attention and the solar system shrank into comparative insignificance.

This intellectual revolution was due primarily to the researches of one of the greatest observational astronomers of all time, William Herschel, whose pre-eminence has recently been recognized by the laying of a memorial stone on the floor of Westminster Abbey. Greatly as he was esteemed by his contemporaries, the full scale of his achievement could not be properly assessed until our own day.

Herschel was a German from Hanover who became naturalized British. It is not as widely known as it should be that in his general conception of the role and nature of the Milky Way he had two immediate predecessors, Immanuel Kant of Königsberg, and Thomas Wright of the County of Durham. It is due to Kant that Wright's name is not forgotten. In 1750 Wright published the one work for which he is famous, a short book entitled *An Original Theory, or New Hypothesis of the Universe*. In this he argued that the phenomenon of the Milky Way, or the Galaxy as it is often called nowadays, is not due to any crowding together of stars but is purely an optical effect. Assuming the star system to which the sun belongs to be much less extended in one particular direction than in all directions perpendicular to it – so that in fact it is more like a bun than an orange – he showed that, if we are somewhere near the centre, then the stars will appear to be distributed with greatest density in a circular band running round the sky, just as the Milky Way does. This effect will be observed even though, in fact, the distances between the stars are on the average the same everywhere.

Kant never actually saw Wright's book, his knowledge of it being entirely due to a short abstract in a Hamburg journal which happened to come his way. He seized hold of Wright's original idea and on it based his *General Natural History and Theory of the Heavens*, which was published anonymously in 1755. Wright's exposition was purely geometrical, whereas Kant's was both dynamical and evolutionary, his object being to show how, on the basis of Newton's law of universal gravitation, the universe might have evolved into its present condition from an initial uniform distribution of particles.

The necessary observational support for the hypotheses of Wright and Kant was provided by William Herschel in the last decades of the 18th century and the first of the 19th. By his investigation of visual binaries, or double stars, he obtained the first definite evidence that Newtonian gravitation operated beyond the bounds of the solar system. With the aid of a more powerful reflecting telescope than any previously constructed he spent many years in his systematic sweeps of the heavens. Herschel's genius lay not only in his ability as a telescope constructor, but also as a visual observer. As he himself said, "Seeing is an art".

One of Herschel's main problems – indeed, his basic problem – was the determination of stellar parallax, *i.e.* the determination of the distances of the stars by measuring the angles of parallax which they subtend at the earth in the course of a year as the earth revolves around the sun. In order to study this problem Herschel found it necessary to investigate pairs of stars which appear to be close together in the sky, although one is a long way off and the other one much nearer. His object was to study the parallactic motion of the nearer star with reference to the more static distant one. But in investigating such apparent visual binaries, he discovered a considerable number of true visual binaries, *i.e.* pairs of stars that are closely related in space and not merely in direction, as seen from the earth.

In the year 1802 he found evidence of the orbital motion of a number of such double stars about each other, and two years later he wrote, "Many doubles must be allowed to be real binary combinations of two stars intimately held together by the bond of mutual attraction". Although, in this way, Herschel extended the range of Newton's law and shifted the main centre of attention of astronomers from the solar system to the stars, he never succeeded in his original object of measuring the distance of any star.

*The quest for stellar parallax*

Some fifteen years after Herschel died, three other astronomers, the German F. W. Bessel, the Scot T. Henderson, and F. W. Struve, a German who had emigrated to Russia, within a few months of each other, in 1838 and 1839, all independently made the first reliable determinations of stellar distances. Even after that, progress was still very slow. Indeed, within the next fifty years hardly more than fifty stellar parallaxes were successfully determined. Now we know more than ten thousand.

As long ago as 1718 the proper motion of the stars had been discovered by Edmund Halley by comparison with observations made in antiquity of four conspicuous stars by Ptolemy, Timocharis and Hipparchus. The ancient observations were all in good agreement with one another. Halley said that these stars, Sirius, Aldebaran, Arcturus and Betelgeuse, "being the most conspicuous in Heaven, are in all probability the nearest to the earth; and if they have any proper motion of their own it is most likely to be perceived in them, which in so long a time as 1,800 years may show itself by the alteration of their places, though it be utterly imperceptible in the space of a single century of years". And, in fact, Halley deduced that these stars had moved in that period of time.

It may seem strange that the star whose distance was first determined was *not* one of the very brightest. Indeed, of the four just mentioned only Sirius is really a near star, the others being conspicuous primarily because of their high luminosity. But the luminosity or intrinsic brightness of a star must be distinguished from its apparent brightness. The former is independent of the distance of the star from the earth. The measure of luminosity is called absolute magnitude, that of apparent brightness apparent magnitude. All stellar magnitudes are measured on a geometric scale so that a difference of one magnitude corresponds to a difference in brightness of approximately 2·512 times, or to be precise the fifth root of 100. Hence, to a difference of five magnitudes in measure corresponds an actual difference in brightness of 100 times. A first-magnitude star is 2·512 times as bright as a second-magnitude star, and so on, the higher the number of the magnitude the fainter the star. The conventional choice of zero-point for the scale is such that the apparent magnitude of Sirius, the brightest star in the sky, is about −1·6, whereas that of the sun is about −26·7.

The absolute magnitude is the magnitude which a star would have if it were brought to the standard distance from us of 10 parsecs. The parsec is the distance at which a star would have to be in order to have an annual parallax of one second of arc. On the scale of absolute magnitude, the sun's magnitude is 4·85, that of Sirius 1·3, and that of Rigel, the brightest star whose absolute magnitude has been reliably determined, about −5·5. Consequently, Rigel is intrinsically much brighter than the sun, in fact about 14,000 times as luminous; Sirius is only about 26 times as bright.

The first star whose distance was reliably determined, 61 Cygni, is comparatively faint, being only of the fifth apparent magnitude. It was chosen by Bessel for a parallax determination because the Italian astronomer Father Piazzi had discovered in 1806 that its proper motion was just over five seconds of arc per year. Because of this unusually large proper motion, 61 Cygni became known as the flying star. Only four larger proper motions have since been discovered, the largest being that of a faint tenth-magnitude star, Barnard's star, which has an annual proper motion of just over ten seconds of arc. Modern research has revealed that the range in observed stellar motions is less than the range in the intrinsic brightness or absolute magnitude of stars, and thus proper motion does, in fact, provide a much better general criterion of distance than apparent magnitude.

For a whole year Bessel measured the changes in the angular distance of 61 Cygni from faint 'neighbouring', but more distant, comparison stars, and at the end of 1838 he announced that, in the course of the year, 61 Cygni had described a very small ellipse in the sky, the image of the earth's path around the sun. The angle which the radius of the earth's orbit would subtend to an observer of 61 Cygni was found to be only three-tenths of a second of arc. Having measured this angle and knowing the distance of the earth from the sun, it was possible to calculate the distance of 61 Cygni, which is about 10 light-years, *i.e.* light travelling at 300,000 kilometres per second would take 10 years to cover the distance, or 3·3 parsecs.

Nowadays all direct determinations of stellar parallax are made photographically. A photograph of the star with reference to its more distant background stars is taken three times at six-monthly intervals. By comparing these three different pictures the proper motion of the star in space is disentangled from its apparent parallactic displacement due to the earth's annual revolution round the sun.

The nearest known star is Proxima Centauri, a companion of the triple system of stars known as Alpha Centauri. Its distance is just over four and a quarter light-years and its parallax a little less than one second of arc. If this three-star system is counted as one star, then there are some twenty-six stars within a distance of four parsecs, or about thirteen light-years, *i.e.* which show an annual parallax of more than a quarter of a second of arc. The approximate average distance apart of stars in our region of space is therefore of the order of five light-years. There are, however, probably several very faint stars still remaining to be discovered in our neighbourhood.

*The nearest stars and the brightest stars*

What are our stellar neighbours like? Of the ten nearest stars to us, counting the sun as one and also taking Alpha Centauri as being three stars, five belong to systems containing more than one star. Sirius, for example, consists of two stars. But only two of the ten nearest stars are of greater absolute luminosity than the sun: Sirius is 26 times as bright and Alpha Centauri 1·3 times. Six of these ten nearest stars have absolute magnitudes not greater than one-hundredth that of the sun. Indeed, of the twenty-six nearest stars more than twenty are intrinsically very much fainter than the sun. Such stars are called dwarf stars.

The list of the twenty or so brightest stars, *i.e.* those of the greatest apparent magnitudes, is very different from that of the nearest stars. Only Sirius and two others appear in both lists. These twenty stars of greatest apparent magnitude include six of absolute magnitude more than 1,000 times that of the sun and one whose absolute magnitude is about 80,000 times that of the sun. Stars of such high intrinsic luminosity are called giants. The nearest, Betelgeuse and Spica, are about 300 light-years away, and it appears, therefore, that in our part of the stellar universe dwarf stars must be much more numerous than giants.

*Stellar luminosities, masses, temperatures and diameters*

Given the distance of a star and its apparent magnitude, its absolute magnitude can be easily calculated. The mass of a star, however, can only be determined if its pull on some other body is known. With the aid of the Newtonian theory of gravitation it is possible to measure the sun's pull on the earth and other planets. Similarly, the mass of a star can only be directly calculated if it is a component of a multiple system.

A surprising result emerges. Although the range of stellar absolute magnitudes is enormous, *i.e.* from less than one-hundredth to more than one hundred thousand times that of the sun, the range in masses is unexpectedly narrow, only between one-fifth and one hundred times that of the sun. Indeed, most stellar masses lie between 0·4 and 4 times that of the sun. For example, the mass of the brighter component of Sirius is 2·44 times the solar mass, whereas that of the fainter component is 0·96 times the solar mass, although the luminosity of the latter is only about one ten-thousandth that of the former.

The determination of the diameters of the stars is much more tricky since the stars, unlike planets, do not show up as discs in the telescope. With the most powerful telescopes even the nearest stars only give diffraction patterns producing spurious, and not true, discs. It was one of the great triumphs of modern observational astronomy when, in 1920, the angular diameter of a star was directly determined for the first time, after A. A. Michelson had suggested that his interferometer be applied to the 100-inch telescope on Mount Wilson. The technique was extremely difficult, but nevertheless the diameters of Betelgeuse and of several other giant stars were determined in this way. The diameter of Antares was found to be about 450 times that of the sun. If Antares were placed with its centre coincident with the centre of the sun, it would extend beyond the orbit of Mars and the earth would be right inside it! Betelgeuse, which also has a very large diameter, oscillates in size, the period of oscillation being about six years. During that time its radius waxes and wanes from about 210 to 300 times that of the sun.

The sizes of these stars are immense, but this was not unexpected. Their empirical determination provided a welcome check for what had been the only, and was to remain the principal, method for determining stellar diameters – a theoretical method based on the hypothesis that the stars could be regarded as perfect, or black-body, radiators. As in the case of the sun, this is not exactly true, but it proves to be a good working hypothesis. On this hypothesis, H. N. Russell of Princeton obtained a formula for the effective surface temperature of a star, involving a factor, known as the colour-index, which has to be determined empirically for each star. Given the effective surface temperature of a star and its absolute magnitude, its diameter can be readily calculated. The problem is simply to discover the size of a surface radiating at this temperature which would have the given luminosity.

The temperature of a star effectively controls what is known as its spectral class. Stars of different surface temperatures have different characteristic spectra. Effective surface temperatures above 50,000 °C. have been determined, and many bright stars have temperatures of 20,000 °C. and upwards, compared with the effective surface temperature of the sun which is just below 6,000 °C.

*The three principal categories of stars*

Roughly speaking, the stars fall into three distinct categories: the main sequence stars, the red giants, and the white dwarfs. The main sequence stars form the leading category, the sun being an average intermediate member. They are, very roughly, of the same size – that is, the same diameter – as the sun. They are characterized by what is known as Eddington's mass-luminosity law, according to which the stars of greater mass are those of greater luminosity, those of smaller mass of fainter luminosity. If the spectral classes (temperatures or colours) are plotted against absolute magnitudes, these stars are found to lie within a fairly narrow band. This was first established in 1913 by H. N. Russell of Princeton following a preliminary indication by E. Hertzsprung of Leiden. The term 'main sequence' is due to Eddington. The brightest main sequence stars have high surface temperatures and are blue or bluish-white in colour.

The other two categories are quite distinct. The red giants are stars of high luminosity, but comparatively low surface temperature. Consequently, they must be enormously large. The brightest and largest in this group, for example Antares and Betelgeuse, are called super-giants. The white dwarfs, on the other hand, are small stars of low luminosity, but high surface temperature. They are comparable in volume with planets rather than with the sun.

Since the range of stellar diameters so greatly exceeds the range of stellar masses, it follows that the range in stellar density must be very wide. The average density of the sun is little more than that of water, whereas that of Antares is less than one-millionth that of water. On the other hand, the average density of a typical white dwarf is 100,000 times that of water.

*Variable stars*

Not all stars are as steady in their behaviour as the sun, which exhibits only a very small degree of variability. Many vary in apparent brightness, the change being often periodic. This variation is sometimes due to external factors: for example, if the star is a component of a multiple system, its light may be eclipsed when it passes behind another star. There are, however, many intrinsically variable stars which may be roughly classified into pulsating and explosive variables. The former are, in the main, giant stars.

The periods of pulsating variables range from about one and a half hours to over a thousand days. Those with periods of less than a day form a very uniform group; they are called RR Lyrae variables after the type-star RR Lyrae. As these stars are believed to be all of very nearly the same absolute magnitude, they are very useful as distance indicators. Variables with periods exceeding one day are called 'classical cepheids', from the type-star Delta Cephei. The adjective 'classical' is added to distinguish them from the RR Lyrae variables, which are sometimes referred to as 'cluster-type cepheids' because they occur in the so-called globular clusters of stars.

The classical cepheids form a much less homogeneous group than the cluster type: they vary greatly in period, luminosity and spectrum. They are of much greater absolute magnitude; indeed, they include many of the brightest stars known. They have even been detected outside our own stellar system and have, therefore, proved to be very useful as long-distance indicators. In 1912 Miss Leavitt of Harvard College Observatory discovered an empirical relation between the average absolute magnitudes of these stars and their periods. Given the period of a known cepheid, its average absolute magnitude can be read off a graph or table, and hence it is possible to calculate its distance.

Explosive variables, or novae, are stars which increase tremendously and very rapidly in brightness; the increase in intrinsic brightness is between ten thousand and a million times and occurs within a period from one or two days up to two or three weeks. After that there is at first a fairly rapid and then a much slower decline. As far as is known, a star *usually* undergoes only one such nova outburst, but it must be remembered that the whole period of telescopic observation is very small indeed compared with the life-times of the stars.

The successive stages in a nova outburst are accompanied by drastic changes in the star's spectrum. As a rule, with the initial rise in brightness the spectral pattern not only changes in character, but moves bodily towards the violet, indicating the rapid expansion of the star. Indeed, the rate of such an expansion can be determined by this typical shift of spectral lines, which is known as the 'Doppler effect', because the measured shift is related to the motion in the line of sight due to the expansion of the side of the star facing the earth. After nova outbursts several novae have been observed to be surrounded by an expanding nebulous envelope, presumably formed by matter ejected from the star.

What is the cause of such violent stellar explosions? When the star is in a steady state, like the sun, there must be, at any point inside it, a balance between the gravitational pressure of the superimposed material and the pressures of gas and radiation. If there is a zone of instability for which such a balance may be easily upset, then a sudden extra liberation of energy in the star, due to some disturbance within it, may cause the star to make a violent transition to a new equilibrium state. Owing to the energy thus liberated, the gas in the star will become overheated, its pressure will rise as it tries to expand, and the overlying layers will be violently ejected into outer space.

Different views have been put forward concerning the kind of star which might be expected to become a nova and the possibility of the sun exploding in this way. Some twenty years ago E. A. Milne suggested that every star must pass through the nova stage at some point in its evolution and ultimately become a white dwarf. On the other hand, D. B. McLaughlin has argued that only special stars become novae and that these stars may be novae more than once. It is difficult to choose between these two hypotheses. It is known that some stars have, in fact, been novae several times. Nevertheless, Milne's suggestion receives some support from the frequent occurrence of novae – in the Milky Way about ten nova explosions are observed in a year – and from a comparison with the number of stars believed to exist in our Galaxy and the age assigned to it. If the sun suddenly became a nova all life on earth would perish rapidly.

There is a class of exceptionally brilliant explosive stars, called supernovae, which at maximum are from between ten to a hundred million times as bright as the sun. If a supernova appeared one hundred light-years away it would shine in the sky more brightly than the full moon. These stars are much rarer than ordinary novae: whereas in a stellar system such as the Milky Way ordinary novae occur at the rate of nearly one a month, it has been estimated from observing supernovae in external systems that one supernova occurs in our Galaxy every four hundred years or so (see Plate XIX). Supernovae have been divided into two classes, one being on the average rather more than two magnitudes (absolute) brighter at maximum than the other.

The only two supernovae which are definitely known to have occurred in the Milky Way are Tycho's star of 1572 and Kepler's star of 1604, and it is thought that these two happened to come so close together in time by pure chance. It is also possible that the Crab nebula (see Plate XX), which is expanding, is the nebulous envelope of a former supernova. From its position in the sky and the measured rate of expansion it has been identified with a very bright star which was recorded by the Chinese in the year 1054.

It is thought that, whereas in an ordinary nova outburst the outer layers of the star are blown off into space, a supernova explosion is much more prodigious, material being ejected not only from the outer layers but even from the deep interior. Spectroscopic investigations indicate that the initial velocities of ejection may be of the order of 5,000 kilometres per second. A supernova outburst may be due to direct stellar collision, but is thought by most astronomers to be a purely intrinsic phenomenon.

### Galactic nebulae

In the course of his observations of the Milky Way Sir William Herschel discovered a number of objects which looked like planets but showed no typical planetary motion. He eventually assigned to them the name planetary nebulae. These nebulae are inside our own system and must be distinguished from those external nebulae which are more appropriately called galaxies to emphasize their similarity with the Milky Way, or the Galaxy. When a planetary nebula is observed with a sufficiently powerful telescope a faint star is usually detected at the centre. Some planetary nebulae are ring-like (see Plate XXI) and their distances vary from 3,000 to 30,000 light-years. The nebulous shell emits light owing to excitation by the central star, which must, therefore, be very hot, its effective surface temperature being from 50,000°C. to 100,000°C. Although the diameters of planetary nebulae are about ten thousand times the distance of the sun from the earth, their masses are less than a fifth that of the sun. They are really great glowing near-vacua thousands of times rarer than the best vacua obtainable on earth. We see them only because they are so large.

The strongest lines in the spectra of these nebulae are certain green lines which for long resisted identification. It was even suggested that perhaps they were due to an element not known on earth, to which the name 'nebulium' was assigned. However, in 1927, I. Bowen found that these mysterious lines were due to doubly ionized oxygen, and that the conditions which are necessary for producing them, namely very low density of gas and exposure to exceedingly weak radiation, are impossible to obtain in the laboratory. Only the great extension of the materials in which these conditions occur enables a strong line to be built up in the spectrum.

Although the central star must be very hot, it is usually rather faint. Paradoxically, although the light from the nebulous envelope can ultimately be traced back to the star, it may be as much as fifty times that emitted by the star itself. This strange effect is believed to be due to fluorescence. The star at the centre is so hot that most of its energy is radiated in an invisible part of the spectrum, in the far ultra-violet. The nebula absorbs this ultra-violet radiation, but re-emits it as visible light. The high surface temperature of the central star, combined with its low absolute magnitude, shows that it must have a small surface area. This conclusion suggests comparison with the white dwarfs. Milne thought that planetary nebulae might have resulted from former novae, but as only about one hundred and fifty planetary nebulae have so far been identified they are too few to suppose that every nova gives rise to such a nebula. The whole problem is still very obscure. The planetary nebulae tend to have definite shapes which are believed to be well maintained by rotational motion about their centres.

Far more numerous in the sky are the amorphous diffuse nebulae in our stellar system. These are of two kinds, the bright and the dark. Bright diffuse nebulae appear to consist of glowing clouds and wisps of matter in chaotic motion (see Plates XXIII and XXIV). Hubble's investigations at Mount Wilson some years ago showed that in almost all cases the light from such a visible diffuse nebula is due to some associated star or stars. These stars are like beacons shining upon a mixture of fluorescent gas (atoms) and reflecting dust (particles of diameters about one hundred-thousandth of a centimetre, comparable with the wavelength of visible light). When the associated star is very hot, having an effective surface temperature of about 50,000°C., the gas fluoresces and an emission spectrum with bright lines is obtained. When the associated star is cooler, its effective surface temperature being less than 18,000°C., the spectrum shows dark absorption lines. In this case the starlight is scattered by the particles and the spectrum of the nebula is simply a reflection of the stellar spectrum.

Generally, the association between a bright cloud of dust and gas and a star or stars is merely cosmographical and not physical. If there is no star in the neighbourhood, the nebula appears as a dark patch in the sky, absorbing and scattering light from stars a long way off. Herschel was interested in such dark patches in the region of the Milky Way and wondered if he was penetrating into the depths of space beyond. Another hundred years or so went by before, towards the end of the 19th century, E. E. Barnard of Yerkes showed conclusively that such dark patches were really obscuring clouds of dust.

Luminous and dark nebulae are often in close association (see Plate I). Dark nebulae are, as a rule, far more extensive than bright ones. Nebulae contain atoms, molecules, dust particles and larger particles, but dust is the main obscuring agent, and its relative amount may vary widely. Indeed, if a given mass

G

of material is to be converted into the most effective obscuring agent possible, it must be split up into particles of this size.

*Interstellar matter*

Most of these obscuring clouds are found in the region of the central band of the Milky Way. Besides these concentrations of dark matter, there is, however, a great deal of more diffuse and rarified obscuring matter in and near the main plane of the Milky Way.

The discovery of interstellar gas goes back to an observation made in 1905 by Hartmann who detected in the spectrum of a certain star in Orion a curious spectral line which differed from the rest. This line was sharp and distinct, whereas the others were all fuzzy, presumably due to the effect of two close stars revolving around each other. In 1909 it was suggested that the sharp line was due to the effect of calcium vapour lying between the star and us. Not until 1924 was it generally realized that this calcium vapour was not an envelope surrounding the star but was truly interstellar. Recent investigators have all come to the conclusion that, in fact, the most abundant interstellar element is hydrogen, but since the interstellar absorption lines of hydrogen, unlike those of sodium and calcium, occur principally in the far ultra-violet, they are not visible. It has been calculated that the mean density of this interstellar gas is about one gram per $10^{24}$ cubic centimetres, which is roughly about one hydrogen atom for each cubic centimetre. This is less than one part in a million of the density of the material in, say, the Orion nebula (shown in Plate XXIV).

*Globular clusters and the size of the Milky Way*

Another useful test for the occurrence of interstellar dust and gas is provided by a different class of stellar objects called globular clusters. These are great spherical conglomerations of stars (see Plate XXV). About one hundred have been identified surrounding the Milky Way. Their masses are thought to be of the order of one hundred thousand times that of the sun. It was observed that the light from the more distant globular clusters was reddened and that this reddening increased with distance.

The observations were consistent with the hypothesis that the reddening was due to the passage of light through interstellar dust, just as the sun looks redder when seen through mist.

The globular clusters are important for the study of the Milky Way because cluster-type cepheids, which are useful as distance indicators, have been identified in them. About thirty-five years ago H. Shapley, with their aid, was able to calculate the distance of the clusters, and he came to the conclusion that they form a system surrounding the Milky Way and concentric with it. Their peculiar distribution in the sky – they are nearly all confined to one-half of the celestial sphere – led him to conclude that the centre both of the system of globular clusters and of the main body of the Milky Way could not be somewhere near the sun, as had previously been thought, but must lie about thirty thousand light-years away in the direction of the rich star-cloud in Sagittarius where the Milky Way is thickest.

As the diameter of the Milky Way in the main plane is now estimated to be about eighty thousand light-years, the sun is very far from being central. The greatest thickness of the Milky Way in the direction perpendicular to the main plane is about one-fifth of the diameter of the main plane, *i.e.* about sixteen thousand light-years, but there is no truly precise boundary, only a falling-off in the number of stars. The diameter of the spherical system of globular clusters is about one hundred and thirty thousand light-years.

### The rotation of the Milky Way

This picture of our Galaxy, which was very revolutionary when first put forward, has received independent support from the study of its rotation. This phenomenon was conclusively demonstrated by the Dutch astronomer Oort in 1927. If the whole system is rotating under its own gravitational field about its centre, and if the main mass of the Milky Way is concentrated towards this centre, then the general motion of the stars in the outer regions should be similar to the motion of the planets about the sun. The outer planets tend to lag behind the inner ones, and similarly in the stellar system the stars which are farther from the centre should lag behind those that are nearer. Hence, stars farther from the centre than the sun should lag behind the sun in this general motion around the centre and those that are nearer should race ahead. By studying the actual motions of the stars and analysing them statistically with this idea in mind, Oort was able not only to show that the Milky Way rotates but also to obtain a general confirmation of Shapley's result that the centre of the system was about thirty thousand light-years from the sun.

Oort's method went further than Shapley's because, being based on the theory of gravitation, it led to an estimate for the total mass of the whole system. The orbital speed of the sun around the centre of the Milky Way was discovered to be about two hundred and twenty kilometres a second. Hence, the sun makes a complete rotation around the centre of the Milky Way in about two hundred and twenty-five million years. From this result the total mass of the system was estimated to be approximately two hundred thousand million times that of the sun. It is thought that this mass is divided more or less equally between stars and diffuse matter which is also subject to the general galactic rotation. Thus, the number of stars in the Milky Way is of the order of one hundred thousand million.

### Galactic magnetism and the origin of cosmic rays

In 1949 Hall and Hiltner, in the United States, discovered independently that the light from some space-reddened stars, *i.e.* stars that appear to be reddened due to intervening material, is also partially plane-polarized. This was interpreted as being due to the effect of a general galactic magnetic field. Previously, there had been no evidence that magnetism featured as an effective galactic force.

One reason why this discovery received so much attention was that soon afterwards Fermi made it the basis of a theory of the origin of the cosmic radiation, which was discussed in Chapter V. Fermi suggested that, provided the particles had fairly high velocities originally (ejection from stars might account for that), the interstellar magnetic field could accelerate them up to the very high velocities observed and also bend their paths round and round, thereby both trapping them within the Milky Way and causing them to impinge on the earth equally from all directions. This ingenious theory, however, is not completely satisfactory. The interstellar clouds would have to be moving relatively to each other with rather larger speeds than have so far been measured. An even more crucial difficulty is that calculation shows that this theory requires the average distance between neighbouring interstellar clouds to be about one light-year. As the average distance between the stars in our neighbourhood is about five light-years, there would have to be more clouds than stars, which appears to be contrary to the facts.

*The spiral structure of the Milky Way*

Nevertheless, the solar system is situated in a very dusty region of the Milky Way and we cannot, therefore, see very far in any direction in the main plane. Since we are also on the out-skirts of the system, it is as though we were attempting to study the lay-out of London on a very foggy day from the roof of a building in the suburbs. The central core of the Galaxy, although believed to be in the direction of the rich star-cloud in Sagittarius, is largely concealed from our vision by dust clouds. These clouds, however, are much less effective in obstructing the passage of radio waves whose wavelengths are from about one thousand to ten thousand million times those of visible light. The development of radio astronomy in the last decade has, therefore, provided a powerful new technique for investigating the general structure of the Milky Way.

About ten years ago van de Hulst, a young Dutch astronomer, predicted theoretically that a well-defined spectral line associated with the neutral hydrogen atom existed in the radio range and, moreover, that it should be readily detectable under the physical conditions prevailing in interstellar space. Each of the two electric charges (proton and electron) which form this atom spins like a top, and so gives rise to a small magnetic field. These two fields can point in the same or in opposite directions. According to van de Hulst, if they point in the same direction then, on the average, after some millions of years the atom will spontaneously switch over to the state in which they point in opposite directions, at the same time emitting radiation of approximately 21 centimetres in wavelength. This line has since been found observationally and has yielded valuable information on the irregular distribution of the interstellar gas, which mainly consists of hydrogen, and hence of the structure of the Milky Way. This investigation indicates that, as had long been suspected on other grounds, our Galaxy is of spiral shape with arms which trail behind as the whole system rotates about its central core. However, for a fuller exposition of present ideas concerning the physical significance of spiral arms we must turn away from the study of our own stellar system and survey regions of the universe beyond the Milky Way.

# CHAPTER X

## The size of the universe

### Beyond the Milky Way

Already in the 18th century, Wright and Kant, in their speculations on the structure of the physical universe, looked beyond the Milky Way. Wright suggested that just as there are other suns besides our own, so there are other galaxies besides the one of which the solar system is a part. Kant developed this conception further. He imagined other systems of stars, each being so far away from us that even with the telescope we cannot distinguish their components. He argued by analogy with the Milky Way that such a stellar world would appear as a faint spot, circular in shape if its plane were perpendicular to the line of sight, and elliptical if seen obliquely. Observational astronomers were already aware of such objects in the heavens and had called them nebulae without knowing whether they were in fact beyond the Milky Way. Here, to quote Kant's own words, "a vast field lies open to discoveries", to which, he added, "observation alone will give the key".

The pioneer of extragalactic exploration was William Herschel with his great reflecting telescope made by his own hands. Then came Lord Rosse with his famous telescope made in Ireland about the time of the potato famine in the eighteen-forties; and finally, in our own day, the astronomers in California with the 100-inch and 200-inch telescopes and all the modern photographic and other ancillary instruments and techniques.

The problem of the nature and status of the nebulae was, perhaps, the most difficult which Herschel tackled, particularly when we recall that he never succeeded in determining the distance of any single body outside the solar system. The complexity of the problem for the pioneer investigator is the more evident when we realize that the term nebulae was originally applied equally to the glowing masses of diffuse material inside our own system and to the globular clusters which surround it, as well as to the other systems which lie outside our own in the depths of outer space. It is not surprising that until some thirty years ago man's ideas concerning the nebulae were characterized by quite as much uncertainty and controversy as still persist today on the even larger question of the universe as a whole.

In 1785 Herschel came to the conclusion that all nebulae were unresolved aggregations of stars outside our own system, thus imagining that he had penetrated the boundaries of the Milky Way. Over thirty years later, in 1817, he admitted that "the utmost stretch of the space-penetrating power of his telescope could not fathom the profundity of the Milky Way". Although he still believed that some distant nebulae were independent stellar systems, the evidence appeared to be confusing and inconclusive.

Nearly half a century was to elapse before one of the great pioneers of astronomical spectroscopy, Sir William Huggins, found that the light from the Orion nebula and some others was similar to that of a glowing mass of gas. Consequently, observational evidence then favoured the view that all unresolved nebulae were merely glowing clouds of gas inside the Milky Way.

Meanwhile in 1845 Lord Rosse had set up his famous reflecting telescope with its 6-foot mirror at Birr Castle in the centre of Ireland. Although such an instrument proved on the whole to be ineffective for the investigation of objects beyond the Milky Way (because, as we now know, these distant regions can only be studied satisfactorily with the aid of photographic methods involving long exposures rather than by visual observers however acute their seeing ability), Lord Rosse was rewarded by one of the great discoveries of observational astronomy. Within a few weeks of its completion, his 6-foot mirror revealed for the first time that the spiral form, so lavishly employed by nature in the organic world, also occurs in the heavens. The Whirlpool nebula (see Plate XXVI) was the first spiral nebula to be recognized as such. Lord Rosse ultimately discovered fourteen similar objects and since then many more have been revealed with improved telescopes and long photographic exposures. By 1918, when the

100-inch reflector was erected on Mount Wilson, it was already estimated that the number of spiral nebulae visible in the heavens must be at least half a million. Nevertheless, despite their enormous number and peculiar structure, all these objects were still thought, particularly by the more cautious observers, to be constituents of the Milky Way. Six years later this conservative hypothesis was to be discarded for ever.

The problem was finally solved by identifying bright stars in the Andromeda nebula (see Plate XXVII). As long ago as 1885 a star had been identified in that particular spiral. In August of that year a new star suddenly appeared in the central region and soon attained a luminosity of about one-tenth of that of the whole nebula. Its position in the nebula and its spectrum, which was quite different from that of a typical nova, showed that it was not a foreground star. In 1917 two other novae were discovered from a study of photographs taken of the same nebula, but they were thousands of times fainter than the object seen thirty-two years before. It followed that if the 1917 objects were typical novae, then the Andromeda nebula must be of the order of a million light-years away and of a size comparable with the whole Milky Way. But if, on the other hand, the 1885 object was a typical nova, then this nebula was comparatively small and near.

Controversy raged until 1924 when, with the 100-inch telescope, Hubble succeeded in identifying cepheid variables in the Andromeda nebula. As mentioned in the last chapter, cepheid variables which are among the stars of highest absolute magnitude had been studied in 1912 by Miss Leavitt, who found an empirical law correlating the average luminosities of these stars and their periods, from which their relative distances can be calculated. But it was still necessary to determine in some other way the distance of one cepheid variable in order to fix the scale absolutely. This was not easy since the nearest cepheids to us in the Milky Way are rather remote; Delta Cephei, the type star, is several hundred light-years away.

On the basis of the absolute scale which was eventually constructed, Hubble assigned a distance of about 900,000 light-years, which was later scaled down to about 750,000 light-years, to the

Andromeda nebula. Since the Milky Way has a main diameter of about 100,000 light-years, Hubble's result showed conclusively that the Andromeda nebula was an independent stellar system of roughly comparable size. Incidentally, this also confirmed the existence of supernovae as objects distinct from ordinary novae. The star observed in the Andromeda nebula in 1885 must have been far more cataclysmic than any ordinary nova, attaining a much greater absolute brightness. Indeed, a supernova can itself become as bright as the stellar system in which it occurs and, if this system is smaller than the Milky Way or the Andromeda nebula, even brighter, as shown in Plate XIX.

*The system of galaxies as a fair sample of the universe*

The determination of the distances of the galaxies, or extra-galactic nebulae, is the basic problem of observational cosmology. After more than thirty years intensive research it remains a subject of baffling complexity. Before considering it further, let us briefly discuss other lines of investigation which support the hypothesis that the galaxies are independent stellar systems.

We have seen that the distribution of stars in our own Galaxy shows a marked tendency to concentrate towards the main plane of the Milky Way. The extragalactic nebulae as actually observed in the sky show the opposite tendency. In fact, there is a zone of avoidance where there appear to be no external galaxies, coinciding with the region where the stars are thickest. No galaxies are seen within a band, varying from 10° to 40° in width, running along the central region of the Milky Way. Outside this band the numbers actually observed are found to increase as the telescope is directed away from the Milky Way towards the galactic poles. Hence, the apparent distribution of galaxies is very different from that of the stars, a result which can be most naturally explained as an optical effect due to the obscuring influence of a zone of dark absorbing material running round the main belt of the Milky Way.

The existence of such a belt of obscuring matter running round the whole system can be seen very clearly in some other spiral nebulae. A good example is shown in Plate XXVIII. It is presumed that there is a very similar zone in the Milky Way, and if we could look at it from outside, from a direction similar to that in which we observe this spiral, its appearance would be similar. When the observed number-counts of the extragalactic nebulae are corrected for the effect of such a zone of obscuration running round our own system, there are no major departures from isotropy, the distribution of the external nebulae being much the same in each direction.

Our relation to the external galaxies must, therefore, be very different from our relation to the stars. The solar system, as we have seen, is markedly eccentric in a large bun-shaped system of stars which rotates with its main plane at right angles to the axis of rotation. With respect to the galaxies, on the other hand, it is more or less centrally situated in a sphere which shows no evidence of any axis of rotation or main plane. In order to study the distribution of galaxies in different directions, instead of relying on the giant reflecting telescopes which pin-point very small areas in the sky, a 48-inch Schmidt telescope which has a much wider angle of vision is now being used on Mount Wilson. With its aid a new atlas of the whole sky is being prepared to a higher degree of apparent magnitude than in any previous atlas, and completed it will be of the greatest interest to astronomers to see whether it confirms the hitherto generally accepted view that the large-scale distribution of the galaxies is isotropic.

On the basis of present observational evidence concerning the extragalactic nebulae the following conclusions can be drawn. Either we are embedded in a super-system of galaxies of such enormous extent that in no direction, even with modern resources, have we any knowledge of the rim, or alternatively, as most astronomers believe at present, the aggregate of galaxies so far observed is a fair sample of the grand system which forms the whole physical universe. In one of his last astronomical lectures Jeans remarked that the history of astronomy is "a history of receding horizons". Here at last we seem to glimpse the ultimate horizon.

## The shapes of the extragalactic nebulae

The spiral used to be regarded as the dominant shape of the extragalactic nebulae: indeed, the term 'spiral nebula' came to be used as a general name for all external stellar systems. Recent observations, however, have shown that the spiral form is by no means the unique shape, or even the most common, elliptical nebulae being more numerous. The situation is somewhat similar to that observed when comparing the apparently brightest stars and the nearest stars, which are in the main quite different. The spiral nebulae, like the brightest stars, are those which are most readily observed because they are the brightest. The elliptical nebulae, which are the more numerous, are smaller and do not show up so readily in the photographs. Although, as their name implies, they appear elliptical in shape, their three-dimensional forms are probably spheroidal. They differ in many ways from spirals. Not only do they possess no spiral arms, but they also contain very little dust or dark absorbing matter.

Plate XXIX shows a fine picture of a typical elliptical nebula taken about forty years ago. Such an object does not look in the least like a system of widely spaced stars, but more like a shining mass of fluid, similar to the appearance of galactic nebulae. Nevertheless, it is well shaped, whereas, with the exception of the very small class of planetary nebulae, the vast majority of galactic nebulae are amorphous objects in chaotic motion and therefore structurally quite different. With the aid of the 200-inch telescope, astronomers can resolve elliptical nebulae readily into aggregates of stars, as shown in Plate XXX.

Besides spiral and elliptical galaxies, there are a number of amorphous structures which are found to be stellar in composition. Prominent among these irregular galaxies are the Magellanic Clouds, two satellite systems of the Milky Way. (The cores of some spirals are bar-shaped, and G. de Vaucouleurs, at Mount Stromlo in Australia, has recently made the revolutionary suggestion that the Large Magellanic Cloud may actually be of this form.) All these different shapes – spiral, elliptical and irregular – occur intermingled in space.

## The nebular clusters

Despite the large-scale uniformity of distribution of the extra-galactic nebulae in all regions of the sky, the small-scale distribution is anything but uniform. The nebulae tend to congregate in clusters, some in small groups of a few and others in massive systems containing hundreds and in some cases perhaps thousands of members.

The nearest and most conspicuous cluster is seen in the constellation of Virgo. It contains some five hundred members. One authority even believes that the local group to which the Andromeda nebula and the Milky Way belong is a sub-cluster of this great system of nebulae. Another well-known cluster is the Coma cluster which is nearly one hundred million light-years away and contains possibly a thousand or more galaxies in a region of diameter between ten and twenty million light-years.

Despite this clustering tendency – many other clusters have been identified besides these two – the ratio of the distances between neighbouring galaxies to their individual diameters is far smaller than in the case of stars. Whereas, apart from individual members of binary and other systems, the stars are, in general, extremely isolated from one another (for example, the distance from the sun to the nearest star is more than twenty million times the sun's diameter), the average distance between neighbouring galaxies is of the order of only ten times their diameters; and the relation between the average distances and diameters of neighbouring clusters of galaxies is of much the same order of magnitude.

Recent statistical tests appear to have eliminated the possibility that the observed distribution of the galaxies, corrected for the effect of the absorbing band around the Milky Way, may be due to some selective effect of viewing associated with intervening interstellar clouds in our own galactic neighbourhood. Instead, it is thought that nearly all galaxies occur in clusters, the spatial distribution of the cluster-centres being more or less uniform. Hence, it seems that these clusters, rather than the individual galaxies, form the principal units of the physical universe.

## The discovery of the two stellar populations

Although very bright stars, such as novae and cepheid variables, were identified in some extragalactic nebulae more than thirty years ago, only in 1943 was it conclusively shown that the elliptical nebulae and the central regions of spiral nebulae are, like spiral-arms and irregular nebulae, also composed of stars. In that year Walter Baade, using the 100-inch Mount Wilson reflector (the 200-inch had not then been completed), finally succeeded in resolving the central region of the Andromeda nebula and also two satellite elliptical nebulae into their stellar components. As already shown, this resolution has since been effected without difficulty using the 200-inch telescope. Nevertheless, Baade's success in 1943 with the smaller telescope was one of the landmarks of modern astronomy, not simply because he had at last verified a result that had long been expected, but because of the method which he employed and the reason he advanced for its success where all previous attempts had failed.

Baade began from the fact that the brightest stars in spiral arms are main-sequence blue stars of high surface temperature. In order to pick out bright stars in the central core of the Andromeda nebula, he therefore began by using blue-sensitive photographic plates. With the sky free from artificial light, owing to the war-time black-out of the neighbouring towns of Los Angeles and Pasadena, and with particularly good seeing conditions in one of the best regions of the world for astronomical observation, it seemed that with the latest blue-sensitive plates success ought to be within reach. Nevertheless, the general fluid appearance of the central region of the Andromeda nebula remained unchanged. It then occurred to Baade to try, instead of blue-sensitive plates, a new type of red-sensitive plate, despite the fact that no red star seemed likely to be detected at so vast a distance when the much more brilliant blue stars had failed to show up in the photographs. With this red-sensitive plate success was immediate. The central core dissolved into myriads of star images. Similarly the companion elliptical nebulae were also immediately resolved into assemblages of stars. It was thus found that, whereas the brightest stars in the spiral arms are blue supergiants, the brightest stars in the hitherto unresolved galaxies and parts of galaxies are red. Moreover, once the threshold of resolution had been reached, these bright stars appeared in great numbers. Their absolute luminosities are about five magnitudes higher, *i.e.* about a hundred times fainter, than those of the brightest stars in the spiral arms. They are, however, distinctly brighter than the red giant stars of our own part of the Milky Way, and are similar to those found in the globular star-clusters which surround the galaxy in a vast system of spheroidal shape.

Baade came to the conclusion that, contrary to previous ideas, there must be what he called two distinct types of 'stellar population', which he called Population I and Population II. Population I is found in the arms of spiral nebulae and in irregular nebulae such as the Magellanic Clouds. With the exception of novae, the brightest stars known are very hot blue stars, and these are all Population I stars. The brightest stars of Population II are considerably fainter. Population II is found in the central regions of spiral nebulae, in elliptical nebulae and in globular clusters. The brightest stars occurring in these are red. As we pass to fainter stars, the two populations show a general tendency to merge when plotted in a Hertzsprung-Russell diagram (luminosity plotted against spectral class). Whether there is an actual merging or not in the case of very faint stars is not yet certain.

Elliptical and irregular galaxies thus have complementary structures and stellar populations, elliptical galaxies being Population II systems and irregular galaxies, on the whole, Population I systems. Spiral galaxies are more complex; they combine the properties of both, the outer arms being Population I and the central regions Population II. If the Andromeda nebula, for example, is photographed in infra-red, the spiral form completely vanishes because it is mainly picked out by the very hot blue stars. Instead we see a spheroidal Population II system, dominated by the central core. This suggests that the Andromeda nebula is a vast system of Population II stars on which the spiral arms of Population I have been superimposed. Photometric studies have shown that, although the arms appear conspicuous on photographs and are dominated by very bright blue stars, they contribute less than one-fifth to the total light emitted by that galaxy.

The contrast between the two types of stellar population extends to their rotational properties and also to their association with interstellar dust. Population I systems rotate and hence are relatively flat, particularly spiral arms, whereas Population II systems show much less evidence of rotation and at the same time are relatively spherical. Even more striking is the association of Population I systems with regions which are rich in interstellar dust, Population II systems being associated with regions which are practically transparent. Baade has shown that the presence of interstellar dust may be directly correlated with the occurrence of highly luminous blue stars. He found such stars in small dusty (light-absorbing) regions inside two elliptical companions of the Andromeda nebula, whereas an otherwise similar third companion showed no trace either of dust or of blue stars.

*The scale of the universe*

Since cepheid variables can be identified only in the nearest extragalactic nebulae, other methods must be found for estimating the distances of more remote galaxies. During the years 1924–1929 Hubble developed a step-by-step technique. First he found that the brightest constituent stars (other than novae) were all of about the same absolute magnitude, averaging about 50,000 times that of the sun. This result provided a criterion for estimating the distances of those nebulae in which individual stars could be detected. Furthermore, most of these nebulae have luminosities between one-half and twice the average, and this result was then used statistically to estimate the distances of still more remote clusters of nebulae. Thus, a provisional distance-scale for the physical universe was built up. It was a rough-and-ready method and was based on a number of bold hypotheses. Nevertheless, Hubble's scale stood the test of time for rather more than twenty years.

Then, quite unexpectedly, in 1952 Baade announced that Hubble's scale would have to be drastically revised – not merely at the uncertain far end, but at the near end, too. Instead of assigning a distance of about 750,000 light-years to the Andromeda nebula, we would now have to regard it as being at least twice as far away. Indeed, the most recent figure that has been suggested is about 1,700,000 light-years. This corresponds to a scale revision factor of rather more than two. There may well be further drastic revisions to come when we are able to make fresh determinations of distances of the more remote nebulae.

Why was this startling revision made? A number of factors led independently to the same result and together they made an overwhelming case. On the old distance-scale, observers had been led to expect that, with the aid of the 200-inch telescope which came into operation in 1949, the globular clusters which surround the Andromeda nebula in much the same way as our own Milky Way is surrounded should be readily resolved, so that their brightest constituent stars (as well as comparable stars in the main body of the nebula) could be studied with ease.

The 200-inch telescope can photograph objects down to an apparent magnitude of 22·5. If the Andromeda nebula were at the distance that had been previously estimated, about three-quarters of a million light-years, then the short-period cluster-type variables in that nebula, and in the globular clusters associated with it, should be of apparent magnitude about 21·8. Consequently, many of these variables (RR Lyrae variables) which are all of about the same absolute magnitude should have been readily detected by the 200-inch telescope. But none could be found on the photographs. With an exposure time of thirty minutes that ought to have revealed these stars quite clearly, there appeared only the brightest Population II stars which are known to be about one and half magnitudes more luminous than the cluster-type variables. Therefore, it looked as if the distance-scale for the Andromeda nebula was wrong by a factor of about two, corresponding to a difference on the magnitude-scale of one and a half. In other words, the Andromeda nebula must be about twice as far away as had previously been thought.

This was not the only line of argument leading to the revision of the extragalactic distance-scale. There were other inconsistencies associated with the old scale. For example, the globular clusters which surround the Andromeda nebula appeared to be systematically smaller than those surrounding our own Galaxy. On the average they seemed to be of only about half the diameter. The discrepancy would disappear if they were twice as far away as previously supposed.

Moreover, the average absolute magnitude at maximum brightness of novae in the Milky Way is about −7·4, whereas that of novae observed in the Andromeda nebula was only about −5·7.

Here again the discrepancy in magnitude is very roughly one and a half. So once more the apparent anomaly could be removed by adopting a correction factor for distance of about two.

The original mistake is thought to have arisen in the determination of the absolute scale of distance, not for the short-period RR Lyrae variables, but for the longer period classical cepheids, those for which Miss Leavitt had obtained the period-luminosity law. As mentioned earlier, the conversion of her scale of relative distances into an absolute scale was based on some independent direct determination of the distance of one cepheid and evidently a mistake had been made. The classical cepheid variables for which the distance-scale was wrong are Population I stars, whereas the RR Lyrae short-period variables are Population II stars. Indeed, Baade's discovery of the new distance-scale was intimately related to his previous discovery of the two stellar populations.

On the old scale it had appeared that our own Galaxy was larger than any other stellar system, a result which had always been regarded as somewhat anomalous. According to the revised calculations, since the Andromeda nebula has been found to be twice as far away as previously thought, its diameter is about twice as great and hence it is larger than the Milky Way. The dimensions of the latter were completely unaffected by the new scale because they had been obtained from the study of RR Lyrae variables in the surrounding globular clusters, and the scale of distance of these remained unaltered. Thus, our own system, although one of the largest of the galaxies, is in fact not the largest of all. According to the latest estimate, based on studying the radio waves from the Andromeda nebula, it is claimed that this galaxy has a main diameter of the order of 250,000 light-years compared with about 100,000 light-years in the case of the Milky Way, but this figure for the Andromeda nebula may not be final.

Baade's revision of the distance-scale had another immediate consequence. With the most powerful optical telescope, the 200-inch reflector on Mount Palomar, galaxies as far away as 2,000 million light-years, about double the previous estimate, can now be observed. We see galaxies up to the present limit of our optical vision, and so far there is no sign of any boundary. It is an awe-inspiring thought that the light waves from the most distant objects which now blur our photographic plates have been travelling for about 2,000 million years and were therefore already three parts of the way to us when the oldest known fossils in our rocks were first being formed. Recently, it has been claimed that radio waves are being received from even more distant objects.

## The masses of the galaxies

It is not easy to determine the total luminosities, or absolute magnitudes, of the galaxies because they are such diffuse objects and their light is not concentrated like that from stars. The average absolute magnitude attributed to the galaxies is of the order of 100 million times that of the sun. On this basis it was estimated that their masses were also about 100 million times that of the sun. But, for various reasons, this is now realized to be an underestimate.

Another line of attack on the problem of determining the masses of galaxies is to study the relative line-of-sight velocities of the members of a cluster. By applying the theory of gravitation to such motions, it was calculated that the average nebula has a mass of about 100,000 million times that of the sun instead of 100 million. The mass of our own Galaxy, deduced from the study of its rotation, is about 200,000 million times that of the sun. A recent investigation indicates that there may be a fairly sharp division between heavy-weight galaxies of average mass about $1 \cdot 5 \times 10^{11}$ that of the sun and light-weights of about $5 \times 10^{9}$ that of the sun. The Andromeda nebula is another example of the former class, whereas according to de Vaucouleurs, who has studied its rotation, the Large Magellanic Cloud is an example of the latter.

## Intergalactic matter

Once the existence of interstellar matter had been established, it was natural to ask whether there is much diffuse matter between the galaxies. Hubble, one of the greatest of all observers in this field, came to the conclusion that extragalactic space is remarkably transparent. Recently, however, evidence has accumulated that in between the different galaxies of a cluster there may be much diffuse matter. F. Zwicky even claims that in the Coma cluster there is an extended mass of *luminous* intergalactic matter of low surface brightness.

An interesting investigation bearing on this question was based on the peculiar fact that some clusters contain a number of galaxies which, although flat like spirals, show no sign of the typical spiral structure nor of the presence of dust which is normally associated with such systems. Baade and Lyman Spitzer suggest that such galaxies may have undergone collisions within the clusters to which they belong and that, in the case of the Coma cluster for example, any one galaxy will experience on the average a collision with another every 120 million years. The effect of the collision of two galaxies would be quite different from that of the collision of two stars, which must be catastrophic like the supernova phenomenon. Two galaxies can pass right through one another with no significant effect on their component stars because they are so very widely dispersed. The main result of repeated collisions will be to sweep out any interstellar matter into intergalactic space. This provides a theoretical argument for believing in the existence of intergalactic matter, at least inside some clusters.

*Newton's universe*

Despite recent spectacular advances in our knowledge of very distant objects, there is no general agreement concerning the full extent of the physical universe, and in particular on whether it is finite or infinite. Conflicting views on this problem can be traced back to antiquity. Aristotle thought that the physical universe must be finite, whereas the ancient atomists, for example Lucretius, believed that there were atoms throughout the whole of infinite space. Lucretius says in his poem, "Space is without end or limit and spreads out immeasurably in all directions alike". During the mediaeval period thinkers tended to follow Aristotle in regarding the universe as finite. The first astronomer to take the step of likening the stars to our own sun and scattering them throughout infinite space was an Englishman, Thomas

Digges, about 1576. This view was enthusiastically adopted by the ill-fated Giordano Bruno, who was burned at the stake for heresy in 1600.

Following the establishment of his theory of universal gravitation, Newton was led, on dynamical grounds, to embrace the idea of an infinite universe. He argued that a finite universe in infinite space would tend to concentrate in one massive lump under its own gravitational attraction. In one of his letters to Bentley in 1692 he wrote, "But if the matter was evenly disposed throughout an infinite space, it could never convene into one mass; but some of it would convene into one mass and some into another, so as to make an infinite number of great masses scattered at great distances from one to another throughout all that infinite space." Nevertheless, he fully realized that this argument presupposed that his law of gravitation was universal. Not for another hundred years, until the researches of Herschel, was it definitely known that the law could be extended beyond the solar system.

In 1895 a peculiar difficulty in Newton's argument was pointed out by the German astronomer H. Seeliger. He began, like Newton, by assuming that matter is more or less uniformly distributed throughout the whole of infinite Euclidean space. He then considered all the matter within a sphere of radius $R$, its mass being proportional to its volume and hence to the cube of $R$. At any point on the surface of this sphere the gravitational attraction towards its centre will be proportional to the mass and inversely proportional to the square of $R$, the distance from the centre. Hence, the attraction will be directly proportional to $R$. If the whole universe is infinite, as Newton supposed, we can consider it as a sphere of infinite radius, but in that case there will be an infinitely intense gravitational field at points infinitely far from its centre. This centre, however, can be chosen to be anywhere we please. It seemed to Seeliger that this argument led to absurdity, and he therefore suggested that, to avoid having infinite gravitational intensity everywhere in space, Newton's law must be modified at great distances. He proposed a new term in this law, which would be effective only on the cosmical scale.

*Einstein's universe*

Twenty years later, a much more profound modification of Newton's law of gravitation was made by Einstein in his General Theory of Relativity, which explained all that the Newtonian theory could account for and several other phenomena in addition. Shortly afterwards, in 1917, Einstein applied his new theory of gravitation to the structure of the whole physical universe. He was so impressed by Seeliger's argument and by other arguments of a similar nature that he took the drastic step of "abolishing infinity". Instead, he maintained that the universe as a whole was finite and unbounded. Its geometry, therefore, could not be the ordinary Euclidean geometry of infinite space but another type associated with a finite, unbounded space. Such a space may be regarded as a three-dimensional analogue of the two-dimensional surface of a sphere. Just as we can travel continuously over the finite surface of the earth without coming to any point where that surface can be said to end, so in a finite unbounded universe there would be no outer boundary of space.

In Einstein's theory, as in all previous theories concerning the structure of the universe, the universe *as a whole* is in a static steady state and shows no overall change with lapse of time. This means that all celestial motions are thought to be negligible compared with the speed of light which plays an important role in Einstein's theory.

In 1930, however, Eddington discovered that Einstein's universe was unstable and would tend either to contract or to expand. Nevertheless, Eddington regarded the finite Einstein universe as the original state of the actual universe and believed that its physical properties determine the laws of nature which control the world as we know it.

Einstein did not assign any precise size to his world-model, but showed that its mass was directly proportional to its radius. Eddington went further and determined a definite value for each. By an ingenious but extremely difficult argument, based on a peculiar conception of the nature of physical measurement, he claimed to obtain a precise value for the number of nucleons and electrons in the world. This number was of the order of $10^{79}$, the corresponding mass being about $10^{55}$ grams. This would mean that there must be enough material in the universe to form roughly a 100,000 million galaxies, each containing 100,000 million stars of average mass equal to that of the sun. The radius of an Einstein universe of this size would be of the order of 1,000 million light-years, but owing to the instability of the system this could only be its initial value. Considerations of this kind show that in analysing the structure of the actual universe we must examine not merely its spatial properties but also the problems of its origin and age.

# CHAPTER XI

# The age of the universe

## The background brightness of the night sky

We have seen how Newton was led by a dynamical argument based on his hypothesis of universal gravitation to the conclusion that matter must be more or less uniformly distributed throughout the whole of infinite space. Furthermore, we have seen how this conclusion led Seeliger some two hundred years later, at the end of the 19th century, to propose a modification in the law of gravitation so as to avoid the paradox of infinite gravitational intensity. Early in the 19th century, however, another German astronomer, H. W. M. Olbers, had already formulated a paradox concerning the intensity of radiation in Newton's universe. He pointed out that an infinite universe of stars uniformly distributed, as envisaged by Newton, would result in infinite sky brightness because, although the apparent brightness of an average star at distance $R$ will vary inversely as the square of $R$, the number at that distance will be roughly proportional to this square, since the surface area of a sphere is proportional to the square of its radius. Hence, if the universe is infinite, it should be observed as infinitely bright.

Although Olber's argument can be modified by allowing for the interventions of clouds of obscuring matter and by making assumptions about the size and the age of the universe, its essential basis is the postulate that both the distribution and the intrinsic properties of radiation-sources are uniform throughout the universe. The argument would collapse if this assumption was modified in some way by introducing a time-effect or a space-effect. For example, a lower intensity might be attributed to a distant light-source at the time when the observed radiation was emitted, than to a similar source observed within our own neighbourhood. Alternatively, the energy of each quantum of radiation from a distant source might be less than that of a corresponding quantum of radiation from a nearby source. Since the energy of radiation is inversely proportional to its wavelength, this reduction would be associated with an apparent increase in the wavelength throughout the whole spectrum which would be shifted to the red. Such a phenomenon could arise if the distant source were not at rest but were receding from us.

### The extragalactic red-shifts

The pioneer of extragalactic spectroscopy was V. M. Slipher of the Lowell Observatory, who in 1912 obtained the first spectrum of the great nebula in Andromeda. This spectrum was shifted towards the blue. When such a phenomenon had been observed in stellar spectra it had usually been attributed to the Doppler effect associated with motion in the line of sight, a blue shift indicating that the source was approaching, a red one that it was receding. Slipher, therefore, assigned to the Andromeda nebula a velocity of approach of about 125 miles, or 200 kilometres, per second. Although high, this was not a fantastic speed to encounter in astronomy; average speeds for different spectral types of star attain nearly 100 kilometres per second. However, by 1917 Slipher had obtained spectra of fifteen spiral galaxies, all but two of which were displaced to the red by amounts corresponding to speeds of recession averaging 400 miles, or 640 kilometres, per second.

Although these speeds were much greater than any previously assigned to the stars in our own Galaxy, the standard procedure of attributing such shifts to the Doppler effect associated with motion in the line of sight was not immediately called in question. Moreover, these speeds were all less than 1 per cent of the velocity of light, and consequently might not have been expected to lead to any serious conflict with the postulate explicitly adopted by Einstein in 1917 when constructing his finite world-model, that the universe in the large is effectively static. Astronomers were, however, perplexed not so much by the magnitude of these velocities as by their orientation, for nearly all were directed outwards, which was difficult to reconcile with the basic hypothesis of the static universe that the proper motions of the galaxies were purely random. A systematic motion of recession, whatever its magnitude, would appear to contradict this hypothesis.

To resolve the question at issue it became imperative to obtain spectrograms of more distant galaxies with the most powerful light-gathering instruments available. Fortunately, the 100-inch reflector came into service on Mount Wilson early in the nineteen-twenties. The task was long and arduous; exposures lasting several nights were necessary and the greatest skill was required to keep the source steadily fixed over the slit of the spectrograph night after night, particularly when, even with this powerful telescope, it remained invisible to the human eye. The resulting picture was often little more than one-tenth of an inch long and one-thirtieth of an inch wide. On such barely perceptible data a new conception of the physical universe was to arise.

Despite the difficulty of obtaining spectra of these remote objects there was no doubt of the reality of their red-shifts. These spectra are dominated by the so-called H and K absorption lines of calcium which are among the most prominant lines in the spectra of stars like the sun. We know that in our own Milky Way the sun is an average type of star, and the extragalactic nebulae, particularly the spirals, presumably contain large numbers of similar stars. The red-shifts are measured by comparing the positions of the H and K lines of calcium in the extragalactic spectra with their position in the solar spectrum. If the shifts are due to recessional motion then the speeds can be immediately deduced from these measurements.

By 1929 Hubble had formulated his brightest star criterion for the distances of those galaxies which lay beyond the region in which cepheid variables could be detected with the aid of the 100-inch telescope. With this method he assigned distances to galaxies outside the local group up to six million light-years. (On Baade's revised distance scale this would now correspond to a distance of twelve or more million light-years.) For all galaxies within this range, but outside the local group (which includes the Andromeda nebula), there appeared to be a definite linear correlation between speed of recession and distance so that, if one galaxy were twice as far away as another, its spectrum would be shifted approximately twice as much. Later, Hubble found that this relationship also applied to more remote nebulae whose distances he had estimated on the hypothesis that there is a definite upper limit to the absolute magnitude of a galaxy. According to the distance scale adopted before Baade's revision, the rate of recession of the galaxies could be expressed roughly as an increase in velocity of recession by about 100 miles per second for each additional million light-years of distance.

After 1929 Milton Humason exploited the potentialities of the 100-inch reflector to photograph the spectra of increasingly fainter and more distant galaxies. Within a few years he obtained a remarkable series of photographs indicating a progressive reddening of spectra with increasing apparent magnitude and distance (see Plate XXXI). At the limits of observation with the Mount Wilson instrument he recorded red-shifts corresponding to velocities of recession up to 25,000 miles, or 40,000 kilometres, per second, *i.e.* velocities up to nearly one-seventh that of light.

Since 1949, when the 200-inch telescope on Mount Palomar came into service, Humason has succeeded in photographing the spectra of even more distant galaxies including those of two members of the remote Hydra cluster. One of these is illustrated at the bottom of Plate XXXI. The velocity of recession corresponding to the red-shift shown in this spectrum is about 38,000 miles per second or one-fifth of the velocity of light. If it were possible to travel in an aeroplane at such a speed we could circumnavigate the earth's equator in two-thirds of a second.

## The expanding universe

The initial hypothesis that the extragalactic red-shifts were due to the Doppler effect associated with motion in the line of sight was not disputed until the early nineteen-thirties when the predominance of abnormally high velocities became apparent. It was clear that a new phenomenon of nature had been discovered and alternative explanations were explored. For example, it was suggested that the shifts might be due to intense gravitational fields associated with distant galaxies, Einstein's general theory of relativity having predicted that strong gravitational fields could give rise to red-shifts. Alternatively, the shifts might be the result of some hitherto unsuspected ageing of light in transmission over the vast distances of internebular space by which it automatically loses energy.

For one reason and another none of these alternative· *ad hoc* hypotheses has received anything like the degree of support given to the original Doppler interpretation and the associated recessional hypothesis. So far there is no observational evidence which can be regarded as directly conflicting with it. An essential feature of the Doppler effect· is that, for a given source of light the ratio of the observed wavelength of any line in its spectrum, for example the H or the K line of calcium, to the corresponding wavelength observed in the laboratory should be the same for all lines. It is not easy to test this feature in the case of extragalactic spectra, but its occurrence in the spectra of some twenty galaxies has been verified to within a probable error of about 5 per cent over a considerable range of wavelengths. In the case of one nebula exceptional accuracy was possible and the feature was established to within 1 per cent.

Much of the objection to the Doppler interpretation of the extragalactic red-shifts has been basically psychological: the velocities obtained were so 'fantastic' that it seemed difficult to believe in their reality. However, they cease to be so incredible if, instead of expressing them in kilometres, or miles, per second or as fractions of the velocity of light, they are considered in relation to the diameters of the galaxies. The earth in its orbital motion around the sun takes ten minutes to pass through a distance equal to its diameter. The sun travelling at about 250 kilometres per second around the centre of the galaxy describes a distance equal to its diameter in about an hour and a half. How long would a distant galaxy, comparable to our own Milky Way in size and receding with one-fifth of the velocity of light, require in order to pass through a distance equal to its main diameter? The time is of the order of half a million years. This way of looking at the problem does not, of course, prove that the Doppler interpretation is the correct one, but it diminishes the psychological objection.

It may seem curious that the most prominent galaxy in the

sky, the great nebula in Andromeda, is an exception to the
general rule and shows a blue-shift in its spectrum. This peculiar
shift is now believed to be primarily due to the fact that at the
present time the rotation of the Galaxy is swinging the solar
system round in the direction of this nebula. More generally,
Hubble's law relating distance and spectral shift does not hold
within the local group of galaxies, presumably because the tendency to individual recessional motion is masked by proper
motions within the local gravitational field of the group. It is
now thought that Hubble's law applies to clusters of galaxies,
and if we regard these clusters as the principal units of the
physical universe, then the universe as a whole cannot be in a
steady state, as both Newton in 1692 and Einstein in 1917
assumed, but instead must be expanding in all directions.

*The origin of the universe*

There are at present two main difficulties in studying the
expansion of the universe. The first concerns the behaviour of
the red-shifts in time, and the second relates to the establishment
of a reliable scale of distance.

We have no direct evidence bearing on the variation of red-
shifts in time because the phenomenon has only been observed for
some thirty or forty years, a minute fraction of the time taken by
light to travel to us from any extragalactic nebula. Nevertheless,
Hubble's law relating shifts or velocities to the corresponding
distances is a spatio-temporal law. For, when we deduce from
observations that a particular galaxy is 500 million light-years
away, what we mean is that it was at that distance 500 million
years ago, whereas all galaxies within the local group are seen
as they were not more than 2 million years ago. The simplest
hypothesis to adopt for the temporal behaviour of the spectral
shift of any galaxy, as it would appear to a sufficiently long-lived
observer, is to assume that it does not change with lapse of time.
Then, on the recessional interpretation, it would follow that the
clusters are all receding from each other with more or less uniform
velocities.

This particular hypothesis was adopted by Milne just over
twenty years ago. He pointed out that any system of bodies

moving uniformly in all directions would in the course of time tend to become an expanding system in which the fastest would have receded the farthest, the respective distances and speeds tending ultimately to obey the law $r=vt$, where $r$ denotes distance, $v$ denotes speed and $t$ denotes time. This law is of the same form as Hubble's empirical law, but provides the additional information that the 'constant' of proportionality in the correlation of speed and distance is a measure of the time that has elapsed since the whole system was in a state of maximum concentration and density.

Guided by this simple way of looking at the situation, Milne then constructed, with the aid of the special theory of relativity, a theoretical world-model in which the galaxies were all in uniform recessional motion from each other. He came to the conclusion that, if this model satisfactorily represented the main features of the actual universe, then all the galaxies must have been compressed together in a comparatively small volume a finite number of years ago, that number of years being given by the empirical value of $t$ in Hubble's law.

The principal uncertainty in the evaluation of $t$ is due to the second difficulty mentioned above, the determination of a reliable scale of distance. When Milne first put forward his theory in 1932, the scale of distance already constructed by Hubble led to the result that the value of $t$ was about 2,000 million years. Milne's theory, therefore, implied that this was the age of the universe since expansion first began.

An alternative theory, advocated by Eddington and others, was based on the idea that Einstein's static universe was in a state of delicately balanced equilibrium between two opposing forces, namely, the binding force of world-gravitation and a disrupting force known as cosmical repulsion, effective only on a very large scale and quite insignificant on the scale of the solar system. As mentioned in the last chapter, Eddington discovered in 1930 that this universe was unstable. A slight radial disturbance would cause it either to expand or contract so that whatever happened it would not return to its original steady state. Eddington assumed that such a disturbance had occurred and that, in fact, the universe was expanding. On this view, expansion and spectral shifts must have been smaller in the past than now, whereas Milne thought they were uniform. The age of the universe according to Eddington's theory was, therefore, greater than according to Milne's.

## *The steady-state theory of continual creation*

In 1948 a radically different interpretation of the observed facts was put forward by H. Bondi and T. Gold, and shortly afterwards by F. Hoyle. According to this hypothesis there is no expansion of the universe, only recessional motion of individual galaxies and clusters. The universe as a whole is in a steady state and was never more compressed than now. There is neither an expansion of finite curved space carrying the galaxies with it, as Eddington believed, nor an expansion of the whole system of galaxies into an infinitely extended space, like a gas dispersing into a vacuum, as suggested by Milne. Instead, according to this new theory, both space as a whole and the system of galaxies as a whole show no temporal evolution whatsoever. Only galaxies and stars pass through the successive stages of an evolutionary history, not the whole universe. As old galaxies and clusters of galaxies stream away from each other, a universal steady state is maintained by the continual and ubiquitous creation of new galaxies to fill up the gaps in space that would otherwise appear as the older galaxies drift apart.

At first the new hypothesis was widely acclaimed. It had several attractive features. From the early nineteen-thirties many men of science had sought to escape from the obvious implications of the successive discoveries of Slipher, Hubble and Humason. The usual line of escape was to seek some alternative to the Doppler interpretation of the red-shifts. The new line of escape was more ingenious. The Doppler interpretation was accepted, but its apparently ineluctable consequence, that the universe as a whole cannot be in a steady state, was unhesitatingly rejected. In order to keep the system going eternally without any overall change, the principle of the conservation of matter on which, for example, modern chemistry was founded by Lavoisier had to be abandoned. Instead, it was suggested that new matter in the form of neutral atoms of hydrogen was continually appearing *out of nothing* spontaneously and more or less ubiquitously in space, although the calculated rate of creation was so small as to be far below any possibility of direct observation.

This theory, at least in its original form, encounters the following difficulty. An old cluster of galaxies – and in due course any cluster, in particular our local group, must age – would acquire by the continual creation of new matter in and around it, an exceedingly powerful local gravitational field which would more than counterbalance the effect of expansion. (It has already been mentioned that there is no evidence of expansion within the local group.) Moreover, this cluster would become ever vaster in extent, without limit. Since the theory presupposes that all regions of the universe are equivalent, this situation should occur statistically everywhere. Furthermore, as it is postulated that there is no evolution of the universe, what will happen in the future must already have occurred in the past. Hence, it follows that there could be no expansion anywhere at any time.

The only escape from this logical *reductio at absurdum* of the theory is to modify the original assumptions. In particular, it has been suggested that when a cluster attains a certain total mass the mere presence of so much matter in a limited volume of space must automatically prevent the spontaneous appearance of further new matter in its neighbourhood. Unfortunately, there is no test for such a hypothesis, since we would require to know what will in fact happen to our own local group in the far distant future and that knowledge is denied us.

Despite these conceptual difficulties, there were certain observationally significant features of the theory which attracted widespread attention. First, owing to there being no world-evolution, the distribution of different types of galaxy in different stages of evolution should be purely random. Thus, distant galaxies, observed as they were hundreds of millions of years ago, should be indistinguishable statistically from those observed nearby as they were only a few million years ago, and indeed the different types of galaxies, irregular, spiral and elliptical, which may represent different stages of evolution, do appear to be all intermingled in the clusters.

*The Stebbins-Whitford effect*

It happened that new observational evidence which might bear on this question of the existence or non-existence of a temporal evolution of the whole universe was first announced in the same year as the steady-state theory was formulated. With the aid of a photo-electric cell and filters which pick out light of different colours, J. Stebbins and A. E. Whitford were able to measure directly the respective total intensities of light in the different parts of the spectrum of a distant source. From the observed bodily shift of the spectrum to the red it was possible to calculate what the colour composition of the light from a distant galaxy should be, but when Stebbins and Whitford used their photo-electric technique to measure this directly they discovered what they called excess-reddening. In other words, they found that the galaxies looked redder than expected, even when due allowance was made for their respective red-shifts. Moreover, this excess-reddening increased with distance. The actual galaxies investigated at that time were all ellipticals, because these are less diffuse objects than spirals and consequently their total radiation was easier to investigate by this technique. Stebbins and Whitford suggested two alternative explanations of this phenomenon. Either the more distant elliptical galaxies are observed as they were at an early stage of world-evolution when they contained more bright red stars than now, or else there is more dust and light-absorbing matter in intergalactic space than had previously been supposed.

According to the steady-state theory, the intrinsic light characteristics of distant galaxies should be the same statistically as of those nearby, and its advocates were therefore obliged to ascribe excess-reddening of distant galaxies to the absorption of light at the blue end of the spectrum by intergalactic matter. On the other hand, as Stebbins and Whitford pointed out, to produce the observed effect far larger quantities of light-absorbing matter would be required than seemed compatible with the apparent transparency of space.

Recently, further evidence has been obtained which tends to support the view that excess-reddening cannot be attributed to intergalactic dust. Whitford investigated distant spirals with the

H

photo-electric technique and found that, instead of showing excess-reddening like the ellipticals, they are actually 'very blue'. He believes that the facts can be explained if the ellipticals had more giant red stars and the spirals more giant blue stars several hundreds of millions of years ago than now. Although further investigation is required, the balance of present observational evidence on the colours of the galaxies is less in favour of the steady-state theory than of evolutionary theories of the universe.

## The distribution of 'radio-stars'

Independent evidence in favour of evolutionary theories of the universe and against the steady-state theory was advanced in May 1955 by M. Ryle and his co-workers in the Radio Astronomy Section of the Cavendish Laboratory in Cambridge. With an exceptionally large radio-telescope completed in 1953, they have discovered nearly two thousand localized sources called 'radio-stars', only one hundred and twenty of which had been known previously. It must be emphasized that these are small regions of the sky from which electromagnetic radiations of radio wavelengths are received. They are probably not stars at all. Some thirty are extended sources, the most intense lying in directions corresponding to the Milky Way, but the directions of most of the fainter sources show no connexion with our Galaxy and are distributed at random all over the sky. In nearly all cases it has so far proved impossible to find visible objects in the same positions. In 1952 Baade succeeded, with the aid of the 200-inch telescope, in identifying two intense radio-stars, one of which was a peculiar interstellar gas-cloud in the Milky Way and the other a pair of remote galaxies in collision some 200 million light-years away. This collision which occurred 200 million years ago gave rise to radio-waves which are now arriving at the earth. The Cambridge radio-astronomers believe that the vast majority of the radio-stars are outside the Milky Way and are caused by the interaction of the gaseous components of colliding galaxies. It seems probable that most of these radio-stars are very distant, lying beyond the range of the most powerful optical telescope.

The most exciting result of the Cambridge survey is that the numbers of these distant extragalactic radio-sources increase with distance more rapidly than would be expected if they were distributed uniformly throughout space. On the basis of evolutionary theories of the universe, this result can be explained as due to the greater frequency of collisions of galaxies in the remote past, whereas on the steady-state theory of continual creation the frequency of such collisions cannot change with time and the observed results are inexplicable. Further confirmation of the Cambridge results and their interpretation is, however, essential before conclusions can be drawn which will be generally accepted.

## The time-scale of the universe

Another observationally significant feature of the steady-state theory concerns the time-scale of the universe. It was argued that evolutionary theories of the expanding universe allowed insufficient time for stellar evolution and for the past history of the earth. Strictly speaking, such an argument could only be legitimately advanced against some of these theories. For, in his last paper to the Royal Astronomical Society in 1944, Eddington calculated that if the expanding universe had originated, as he believed, in an unstable Einstein universe, its present age would be of the order of 90,000 million years. On the other hand, it is true that by 1948 the apparent inadequacy of time-scale was a serious embarrassment for those who supported any theory of the expanding universe such as Milne's, which involved the interpretation of Hubble's constant as a measure of the present age of the universe. The then accepted value of this constant was such that the age came out to be about 2,000 million years. But a careful analysis, two years previously by Holmes, of the radioactive minerals in the earth's crust had led him to conclude that the most probable age of the earth's surface was about 3,350 million years. Despite the uncertainty of the data, this figure came to be generally accepted as a fairly reliable estimate and it was thought unlikely that the age of the earth could be much less. Consequently, astronomers were confronted with the anomaly that the age of the universe on the simplest expansion theories was less than the age of the earth!

According to the steady-state theory, no such difficulty could arise since the universe as a whole was presumed to have an infinite past. At one time it was even claimed that only the steady-state theory could cope with the facts. However, one of the immediate consequences of the new distance-scale for the extragalactic nebulae, announced by Baade in 1952, was that the empirical value of $t$ in Hubble's law, $r=vt$, had to be doubled since $r$ was doubled and $v$, being deduced directly from the red-shift, was unaltered. Hence, the age of the uniformly expanding universe, which is equal to $t$, had to be increased from about 2,000 to about 4,000 million years. According to the latest work, it may be that Baade's scale-factor will have to be still further increased, in which case the age of the expanding universe will perhaps be 5,000 million years or even more.

The dramatic revision of the distance-scale, and hence of the time-scale of evolutionary world-models, removed the previous anomaly concerning the relative age of the earth, and at the same time demolished one of the most cogent arguments for the steady-state theory. Indeed, not only were evolutionary theories of the universe restored to favour, but several independent lines of enquiry showed a remarkable convergence to the same epoch in the past.

Main sequence stars which, like the sun, are thought to generate their energy by thermonuclear reactions are estimated to have existed for up to 5,000 million years. Estimates for groupings of stars, which range from binaries to vast clusters, are based on consideration of the external influences which tend to disrupt them. It has been calculated that the disturbing effect of the Galaxy as a whole on close binaries, for example, has not been acting for more than 10,000 million years at most. The estimated ages of open star-clusters suggest that this figure of 10,000 million years is an upper limit and can probably be reduced to one-half or less.

Globular star-clusters, which are Population II systems, show every sign of great age. They are highly compact (see Plate XXV) and have life-expectancies of more than 10,000 million years. Moreover, they contain no very hot highly luminous stars which burn up their energy comparatively rapidly. Theoretical considerations based on the actual range of stars found in globular clusters lead to the conclusion that all the constituent stars are of about the same age. We have, therefore, strong reasons for regarding these clusters as assemblages of stars formed some four or five thousand million years ago.

Turning from clusters of stars to clusters of galaxies, calculations made of the time for which they can be expected to hold together under their gravitational attractions lead to life expectancies ranging up to about 10,000 million years. These calculations are based on measurements of their internal motions, and these are deduced by comparison of the respective red-shifts of their component galaxies. The fact that so many clusters of galaxies are still observed again suggests that their age is unlikely to be much more than 5,000 million years.

Another line of enquiry pointing to a comparable result concerns the natural radioactive elements. Their very existence at the present time as elements which spontaneously decay implies that they have not always existed in their present form. The observed uranium-lead abundance ratio (see Chapter II) and the half-lives of uranium and thorium are consistent with each other and with the age attributed to the universe. If one assumes that radioactive isotopes were equally abundant when formed, then from their present observed relative abundances one may calculate the epoch of formation. The elements that have half-lives of the order of 10,000 million years, such as uranium-238 and thorium-232, are still abundant on the earth, whereas isotopes of shorter half-lives, such as uranium-235, are much rarer. Calculations show that uranium-235 and uranium-238 would have been equally abundant about 4,000 million years ago.

Thus all the available evidence points to the conclusion that there was a critical epoch in the history of the universe some 5,000 million years ago when it assumed the form which we now study.

## The origin of the elements

Throughout the universe there is on the whole extraordinary uniformity in the relative abundances of the elements, although planets like the earth are exceptional. This lends strong support to the hypothesis that the elements were formed in the pre-stellar stage uniformly throughout the universe. Canon G. Lemaître of

Louvain has suggested that the whole universe began as a single giant particle of density about $10^{14}$ times that of water. When expansion started it became unstable and broke up rapidly into fragments. Lemaître likens the evolution of the universe to a display of fireworks, of which the cosmic ray particles are a present reminder of past glories. A serious objection to this theory is that, although it can explain the origin of the heavy elements, it provides no satisfactory explanation of how the lighter elements were formed.

An alternative theory, due to G. Gamow and others in America, is based on the idea that the universe began as a hot nuclear gas at a temperature of thousands of millions of degrees so that all matter was in the form of the simplest particles – protons, neutrons and electrons. Owing to expansion, this gas became both less dense and much cooler and neutrons became attached to protons to form complex nuclei, the prototypes of the atomic nuclei of today. In order to account for the observed relative abundances of the different elements, the conditions of temperature and pressure at this stage would have required delicate adjustment. The principal difficulty of the theory, however, arises as a direct consequence of the fact that it entails a step-by-step process of successive neutron capture to build up the more complex nuclei from the simplest. Owing to some peculiar interplay of nuclear forces, neither a single proton nor a single neutron can be attached to the helium nucleus, of mass 4, to obtain the next isotope, of mass 5. There is, in fact, no isotope of mass 5. Hence, to build up an isotope of mass 6, two particles must be captured simultaneously by a helium nucleus. Unfortunately, under the assumed physical conditions, the probability of this happening is negligibly small. It is possible that this difficulty may eventually be overcome, without special *ad hoc* hypotheses, by more detailed study of the self-heating of the nuclear gas, but the calculations are likely to be extremely complicated. At present this theory cannot be regarded as more than a bold hypothesis.

It has been suggested that heavy elements may be built up from lighter elements by the peculiar physical conditions associated with the supernova explosions.

*The origin of stars*

Whether the galaxies and clusters have existed throughout the entire history of the universe, or whether they condensed out of a universal primaeval gas at an early stage in cosmical evolution, is an open question. There is somewhat more evidence bearing on the origin of individual stars than on that of galaxies, although it seems probable that the two problems are closely linked. All the available facts indicate that at the present time of observation star formation is confined to irregular galaxies and the arms of spirals, which are Population I systems. These systems contain large quantities of dust and gas from which stars may be generated by condensation.

It has been suggested that a spiral galaxy may be an irregular galaxy rotating within an elliptical galaxy and thereby swirled into the spiral form. As already mentioned, when a typical spiral, such as the Andromeda nebula, is photographed in the infra-red, the spiral shape is no longer seen and the galaxy appears to be a vast system of spheroidal shape. This strongly suggests that the spiral arms, which appear so prominent in the usual photographs because they contain the most luminous stars, are minor attachments to the main body of the system in which they occur. Moreover, they are probably comparatively short-lived. Study of the spectra of light from different regions in the arms shows that they revolve about the central core with speeds depending on distances from the centre. The outer regions revolve more slowly than the inner regions, just as in the solar system the outer planets revolve more slowly around the sun than do the inner planets. Hence, if spiral arms persisted for several revolutions, they would tend to become twined up. In fact, the arms usually show only one or two complete turns, indicating that, in all probability, they are young, transitory features of the galaxies in which they occur.

This conclusion accords with the fact that, being Population I systems, spiral arms are dominated by highly luminous energy-spendthrift stars. Indeed, some super-giant stars have a total life-expectancy of the order of only a million years and must, therefore, have been formed very recently. It is highly probable that stars like these are still being formed in our part of the

Milky Way. For the emergence of new stars, we must look to the thickest dusty regions. Baade directs our attention particularly to the great cloud complex of which the Orion nebula is the most conspicuous feature (see Plate XXIV). He suggests that the creation of new stars may actually be in process in very dark parts of this region. It may be that Population I stars are formed from Population II, by interaction with interstellar matter.

*Stellar evolution*

Many different views are held on the fascinating problem of stellar evolution, and this is not surprising when we consider the extremely limited data on which we have to work. All our knowledge of stellar interiors is inferred by long and complicated trains of argument based on abstract theory, observations of stellar spectra and laboratory physics. Moreover, no relevant spectroscopic data were obtained earlier than the 19th century, and when we compare this limited range of time with the vast period involved in the history of a star such as the sun, running into thousands of millions of years, we immediately see how narrow is the empirical foundation on which we have to build. To complicate matters further, it is almost certain that the problem of the evolution of the stars, like that of their origin, is profoundly influenced by the even vaster problem of the origin and evolution of the galaxies in which they occur.

It is often assumed that the mechanism of stellar evolution consists simply in the burning up of all available hydrogen, and perhaps heavier elements, until these processes are no longer possible (it is probable that only a fraction of these elements can be consumed steadily in this way). The star then explodes in a *nova* outburst, the remnant slowly progressing afterwards through the white-dwarf stage until a final black-dwarf state of total darkness and extinction is reached. The fact that white-dwarfs appear to be very numerous, at least in the neighbourhood of the sun, lends support to this hypothesis, but there are reasons for believing that the white-dwarf state is not possible for masses exceeding that of the sun by more than about 50 per cent. Perhaps the *supernova* explosion is the drastic means by which the larger stars ultimately shed their superfluous mass.

Observations by Baade and Minkowski on the Crab nebula (Plate XX), which is believed to be the remnant of a supernova, indicate that the central star is of white-dwarf size, whereas the mass of the surrounding nebular matter is several times that of the sun. Of the two classes of supernovae, the brighter are thought to be Population I stars and the others Population II.

## The laws of nature

Surveying the universe from the solar system out to the farthest depths of space, scientists have boldly applied the fundamental laws of physics to cover immense distances of space and correspondingly enormous stretches of time. The extrapolations from direct observation and laboratory experience which are involved have been described by a distinguished American physicist and philosopher of science, P. W. Bridgman, as "hair-raising". With what degree of confidence, then, can we accept the pronouncements of modern astronomers and cosmologists on the structure of the universe, and in what way, if any, are their views to be regarded as better founded than those which were held in previous centuries by men of equal intelligence?

In a famous lecture on the origin of the solar system, delivered over eighty years ago when knowledge of the structure of matter and of stars was far less extensive than today, the great German physicist and physiologist Helmholtz justified the study of the subject despite its predominantly speculative nature. He argued that, far from avoiding problems of cosmogony, scientists were not merely entitled to consider these problems but should regard it as their duty to study them. They should investigate whether "on the supposition of an everlasting uniformity of natural laws, our conclusions from present circumstances as to the past ... imperatively lead to an impossible state of things; that is, to the necessity of an infraction of natural laws, of a beginning which could not have been due to processes known to us". Considered as a question of science, this, he maintained, was no idle speculation, for it concerned the extent to which existing laws are valid.

The principle of extrapolation of the laws of nature which have been empirically tested in the laboratory and by observations on the solar system is often called the 'principle of the uniformity of nature'. The crowning achievement of Isaac Newton was to provide compelling arguments for extending laws, governing physical phenomena here on earth to the heavens. For two thousand years the contrary opinion of Aristotle had prevailed. His separation of the terrestrial and celestial realms was, however, not the purely arbitrary imaginative hypothesis that it is nowadays so often made to appear. It was partly based on sober empiricism. "It is absurd", he wrote, "to make the universe to be in change because of small and trifling changes on earth, when the bulk and size of the earth are surely as nothing in comparison with the whole universe."

The extrapolation of physical laws from the terrestrial scale to the cosmical is both a hypothesis and a method of investigation which has continually to justify itself by results. So far from being mere 'common sense', it has on occasion led great men of science to accept the most fantastic conclusions. An outstanding example was Sir William Herschel's belief in the habitability of the sun.

The Copernican conception of the earth as a planet provided a powerful argument for believing that similar physical processes to those occurring on earth prevailed on the other planets, and it was natural to conclude that since the earth is a habitable globe the other planets must be too. Nowadays we discriminate more carefully between the uniformity of physical laws and of physical conditions. The belief in the uniformity of the universe and the plurality of worlds led Herschel, in a memoir *On the Nature and Construction of the Sun and Fixed Stars* published by the Royal Society in 1795, to argue that the sun is an overgrown planet with an abnormally luminous atmosphere. Below this atmosphere the main body of the sun was, in his opinion, opaque and of great solidity. This idea was not pure speculation. It was based on the observation that sun-spots appear dark against the general bright background of the solar surface. We now believe that this is because the spots are regions of somewhat lower temperature, but Herschel suggested that they were regions where we look right through to the solid surface beneath the sun's atmosphere. Moreover, he thought that this surface was diversified with mountains and valleys. "I think myself authorized", he wrote, "upon astronomical principles to propose the sun as an inhabitable world". He based this conclusion on the essential similarity of the sun and planets! "Its similarity to the other globes of the solar system with regard to its solidity, its atmosphere and its diversified surface, the rotation upon its axis, and the fall of heavy bodies, leads us on to suppose that it is most probably also inhabited, like the rest of the planets, by beings whose organs are adapted to the peculiar circumstances of that vast globe."

To meet the common-sense objection that, in view of the heat which we receive on earth from the sun, the inhabitants of the sun's solid surface could not be protected by a mere blanket of cloud from being roasted, he again appealed to the uniformity of natural laws. He pointed out that high up in our own atmosphere, where there is less to impede the sun's rays than on the earth's surface, it is actually colder. Writing only eleven years after the first successful aeronautical ascent in 1783 and in the same year in which the first military balloon was used, by the French for reconnaissance before the battle of Fleurus, Herschel not only refers to the temperature on mountain tops but also to the fact that "our aeronauts all confirm the coldness of the upper regions of our atmosphere". Thus, arguing from correct observations and plausible hypotheses in a manner which he was convinced was strictly scientific, the greatest astronomer of his age drew conclusions concerning the nature of the sun which were no less fantastic than Aristotle's idea that it was a 'perfect body' in which change and decay could never occur.

Encouraged by Helmholtz's exhortation, but also warned by the example of Herschel's fallacious application of the principle of uniformity, how are we to assess the far-reaching conclusions concerning the physical universe drawn by contemporary astronomers and cosmologists? Of the hundred thousand million stars which form our Galaxy, only the sun is sufficiently near to us for direct observation of surface details. Our ideas concerning the surfaces of all other stars, as well as of their internal structures, are inferences dependent on our conception of physical laws. When we come to consider the universe as a whole and in particular its origin and age, fundamental questions concerning the nature and scope of scientific method and of the laws of nature force themselves upon us.

Newton was fully aware of this aspect of the cosmological problem and of the hypothetical nature of the principle of uniformity. In one of the Queries inserted at the end of his *Opticks* he was careful to point out that "it may also be allow'd that God is able to create Particles of Matter of several sizes, and in several Proportions to Space, and perhaps of different Densities and Forces, and thereby to vary the Laws of Nature, and make Worlds of several sorts in several parts of the Universe. At least, I see nothing of contradiction in all this."

Nevertheless, although astronomers can give no final answer to the vast problems of cosmology and cosmogony, in particular the problems of the origin and age of the universe, they now stand at a much better vantage point than did their predecessors. Of course, it is still just as true now, as when Newton wrote, that the principle of uniformity of natural laws is a hypothesis and it is just as true now, as when Helmholtz wrote, that no theory concerning the origin of the world can be verified by direct observation, yet it seems remarkable that so many independent lines of enquiry into the history of the earth, the stars and the galaxies all point towards the same epoch in the past. This convergence of different methods of dating, each of which involves an enormous extrapolation from present observations, is itself the best answer to those who are sceptical of the results of each investigation considered separately, and strongly suggests that the universe has a finite age of some five thousand million years. Whether this is to be taken as the time that has elapsed since the whole physical world was created or only since it took the form which we now study is a question which takes us beyond the limits of scientific enquiry. 'Our conclusions from present circumstances as to the past' leads us to regard this as the longest stretch of past time over which we can extend the laws of nature as we know them. Beyond that we cannot penetrate.

# Appendix

*Theories and the role of mathematics*

It is generally known that mathematics and physics are intimately bound up. Every physicist has to have training in mathematics, and a practising physicist may use mathematics as often as he uses a measuring instrument. The non-mathematical reader cannot be expected to follow the mathematical arguments with which the physicist works, but he can gain some understanding of the role of mathematics in physics.

First, he should understand that mathematics is not a method by which the scientist "draws truth out of the sky". It is, in the first instance, a shorthand by means of which the results of experiments can often be expressed concisely. For example, one of the most important of physical laws is Newton's second law of motion

$$F = ma,$$

where $F$ stands for the force acting on a body, $m$ for its mass, and $a$ for its acceleration, or rate of increase of velocity.

The formula given above makes use of algebraic symbolism. Thus $F$, $m$ and $a$ really stand for 'hidden' numbers, like '$x$' in elementary algebraic expressions. The significance of a given $m$, for example, is that it represents that number of the particular units which have been chosen as convenient for the measurement of mass. The units must be chosen to be consistent with each other; then by the use of this formula we can find what would be the acceleration of a body of known mass under the action of a given force.

But mathematics has a wider application than we have so far illustrated. For there can be formulae of all kinds in physics, relating more and more physical observations. By making use of the well-known techniques of algebra we can sometimes establish links between several formulae, and perhaps arrive at conclusions quite distant from those which could be established in any given experiment. The Thomson experiment which was discussed in the Introduction contains quite a good example of this. In fact, it consisted of two experiments; in one, the effects of magnetic and electric forces were 'balanced', as already described. In the second, the actual deflection due to a lateral magnetic force was measured.

Considering the first experiment only at present, we have to make use of the known physical fact that the force upon a particle carrying an electric charge $e$ moving with velocity $v$ at right angles to the direction of the field of a magnetic force $H$ is equal to $Hev$.

Similarly for the effect of electric force, we know that the force on a charge $e$ in a field of electric force $E$ is $Ee$. If the two forces are balanced, we therefore have

$$Ee = Hev,$$

and so $$v = E/H.$$

The second experiment enabled Thomson to find the value of $e/m$. It was necessary to make use of another known physical fact: that a force $F$ acting at right angles to the direction of motion of a particle of mass $m$ moving with velocity $v$ deflects it along a circular path of radius $r$, such that $F = mv^2/r$, whence

$$r = \frac{mv^2}{F}$$

In this case, we know that $F = Hev$, so that $r = \dfrac{mv}{He}$.

By combining this with the previous formula, again using ordinary algebraic operations, we find

$$\frac{e}{m} = \frac{E}{H^2 r}.$$

The value of $r$ could be worked out, using further simple mathematical arguments, from the value of the deflection observed and the length of the path of the beam between the parallel plates, and hence a value obtained for $e/m$. Incidentally, it will be noted that $v$ 'drops out' of the argument. It is not in itself a fundamental property of the electron but depends upon the voltage applied between the terminals of the discharge tube.

The degree of complication in modern physics requires the use of mathematics which is much more difficult than the elementary algebra used above. In particular, it involves constant use of a powerful mathematical tool known as 'calculus'. Its scope can be illustrated by an example. It is easy to work out the velocity at any time of a falling body. For the acceleration, or rate of increase of velocity, of a falling body on the earth is a *constant* quantity, 981 centimetres per second per second (or 32 feet per second per second), denoted by $g$. Then after time of fall $t$ the velocity $v$ is given by

$$v = gt.$$

But how can one work out the *distance* fallen after a given time, remembering that the velocity (that is, the rate of traversing

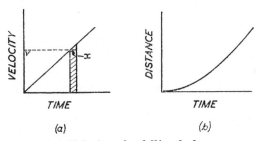

Fig. 31. (*a*) *Velocity of a falling body.*
    (*b*) *Distance travelled by a falling body.*

distance) is not constant but increasing continuously? The answer can be found graphically. The variation of the velocity with time is correctly represented by a graph of the form shown in Fig. 31 (a) in which $v$ is plotted against $t$, that is, the velocity increases uniformly (or, as we would say, *linearly*). During a small interval of time $x$, the distance fallen is nearly equal to $xv$, where $v$ is the velocity at, say, the beginning of the interval. It can thus be represented by the shaded area. Clearly, therefore, the distance fallen at any time can be represented by the total area under the line up to that time, when appropriate consideration is given to the matter of units. If we measure this area we find, for example, that the distance fallen is related to the time by a graph of the form shown in Fig. 31 (b).

The function of the calculus is to extend the scope of algebraic symbolism and operations to cover such problems as the derivation of the form of one of these graphs from the other, or *vice versa*, without the necessity for, say, the actual measurement of areas. By the use of such methods we should be able, for example, to work out the motions of electrons in tubes containing complicated assemblies of plates which need not be parallel, under circumstances in which the magnetic or electric forces were not fixed but varying, as in alternating current. This is indeed one of the main problems in electronics. It was by such an approach that methods were devised during the war for generating powerful beams of radio waves of wavelength sufficiently short for use in radar; that is, fairly short compared with the size of the object – the aircraft – being looked for.

The use of graphical methods of representation is very common in science. It is essentially a corollary of the method of mathematical representation. For example, if certain new experimental observations are made it is often much easier to represent them by drawing a graph than to find an appropriate mathematical formula. It is significant that at scientific conferences, where the presentation of new results occupies much of the proceedings, the speakers usually bring with them lantern slides on which their results are graphically represented. The reader will be familiar with the use of graphs in, say, the reports of companies, or in election manifestos. If he has the habit of drawing a graph of the fluctuations of his own bank account he may have a very realistic knowledge of the significance of negative values.

But mathematics is even more important in physics than this. Not only can the mathematician deal with problems, such as those just mentioned, concerned with the interpretation of experiments or the forecasting of behaviour in particular pieces of apparatus; he can also treat natural objects as pieces of apparatus. For example, knowing as he does that a hydrogen atom consists of a negatively charged electron and a positively charged nucleus (or proton), he can apply the formulae already discovered in ordinary laboratory experiments, relating the motions of charges with the electrical and magnetic conditions, to try to predict the behaviour of hydrogen atoms. The results of such enquiries might agree with the experimentally observed facts about the behaviour of hydrogen atoms. (Actually they do not, as we have seen.) If they did, he would decide that his idea of the structure of the atom was more or less complete, and that its constituent parts obeyed the same rules as do the larger objects studied in ordinary laboratory experiments.

In physics today there is a continuous interplay between mathematics and experiment of the kind implied here. Indeed, mathematics in physics has become so important, and so complex, that there now exist mathematical or theoretical physicists who are expert in mathematical techniques rather than in experimental techniques. Sometimes discoveries are, in a sense, first made by the theoretical physicist and later confirmed by the experimenter. Probably the most famous example of this was the discovery by J. Clerk Maxwell that the general formulae connecting electric and magnetic phenomena, when combined, appeared to indicate that electromagnetic waves must exist, before radio waves had been experimentally discovered. On other occasions the experimenter first makes his observation, and it is later explained by the theoretician. Of course, the ordinary experimenter also tries to be a theoretical physicist as far as his mathematics and his opportunities allow, and he can usually cope with the simpler situations. For example, he is usually adept at spotting whether results expressed graphically imply some simple mathematical relationship between the quantities under consideration.

### Laws, hypotheses and theories

It is very easy in discussing the foundations of physics to try to introduce distinctions between the terms law, hypothesis and theory which are not really of great significance. The main truth about physics, experimental and theoretical, is that its direction is always towards the discovery of new facts and the arrangement of new and old facts in as simple a scheme as possible. When it is possible to express in a single statement or formula the key to a large number of experimental situations it is common to attach to it the status of a 'physical law'. We have already had an example of a formula ($v=gt$) which covers a large number of situations in that it tells us how the velocity of fall of *any* body towards the earth would increase with respect to the time of fall. However, this might not be thought of sufficient general significance to qualify as a physical law. A more general statement would be one which defined how bodies accelerated when under the action of *any* force, not necessarily gravitational, and not necessarily steady; this is, of course, Newton's second law of motion which has already been discussed.

The great conciseness of mathematical statements makes them ideally suited to the formulation of physical laws, and very many of the laws of physics are expressed in mathematical form. It would be a mistake, however, to suppose that only mathematical statements are important. It is in an equal sense a law of physics that electrons have been identified to have many properties typical of particles, and this statement can be made without mathematical symbolism.

It is also misleading – although it rarely leads to any worse effects than an expenditure of time upon philosophical or metaphysical discussion – to suppose that the use of the word 'law' implies compulsion. The scientist would normally consider the significance of this term to be simply that which it has here been given: a physical law is a concise summary of the information derived from a multitude of experimental observations in which some common feature is picked out.

But, the philosophically inclined reader might insist, what happens if on some occasion the law is not 'obeyed'? Can any law be obeyed without exception unless there is some compulsion? The scientist might try to disregard the second question. To the first he would probably say: if a 'law' is not obeyed, even on a single occasion, it is no law. He would wish to check in detail the circumstances surrounding the exceptional observational in order to make sure there had been no error, and would probably repeat the experiment many times. This would be partly in order to see whether there might be another failure to obey the law, but more important, to give him an opportunity to watch for any intruding element in the experiment which might affect the result. As a matter of fact, it has often been in situations of this sort that new discoveries have been made in physics. The intrusion is often the most interesting thing in the experiment.

It may sometimes happen, when an experimental situation is carefully examined in such a way, that the accepted relevant laws are found to be nearly but not quite correct. This is a particularly interesting state of affairs. A *systematic* departure from the accepted law suggests that some finer detail remains to be discovered. A very important example was the discovery, frequently discussed in this book, that mass and energy are interchangeable. For a long time it had been accepted that energy was conserved – that is, it was indestructible. If it disappeared in one form it must re-appear in another form. For example, when the kinetic energy of the water falling over a waterfall disappears at the bottom, it re-appears as heat energy and the water rises slightly in temperature. This general principle was known as the law of conservation of energy. Equally, it was thought to be obvious that matter was indestructible and therefore that *mass* must always be conserved. It is now known, of course, that under certain circumstances, mass can be converted into energy, and *vice versa*. So the law has to be altered or restated. We must either retain the law of conservation of energy with the stipulation that mass is one of the forms of energy now to be considered, or perhaps state a new law of the conservation of mass-energy. In either case we shall certainly have to 'repeal' one law and lay down another. This does not worry the scientist as much as it might worry the philosopher who has been following his work. In science, the experimental fact takes first place.

There is another lesson to be learnt from the example of the waterfall. For where does the kinetic energy of the water come from in the first place? Of course, we know that the water is accelerated because of the force of gravity. But in order to allow the law of conservation of energy a general validity we have to invent a new form of energy and say that the 'potential' energy of the water at the top of the waterfall has been converted into kinetic energy at the bottom. This would be called gravitational potential energy; other examples of potential energy (elastic energy in these cases) would be the hidden energy in, say, a compressed valve spring, or the stretched rubber of a catapult, which could at any time be converted into kinetic energy.

The term 'hypothesis' is usually used in physics to refer to assertions of the same kind as those made in stating physical laws, but thought at the time to be provisional, or temporary, in character. In other words, a hypothesis is an intelligent guess. The results of further experiments would be expected, ultimately, either to confirm hypotheses and give them permanent status as laws, or to dispose of them as unprofitable or useless.

The term 'theory' is not always used with any precise intention. This word is very commonly used in connexion with rather large-scale mathematical treatments, such as exist in the theory of relativity or the quantum theory – to name two theories which are well known by name – and cover a large number of experimental situations. However, it is also used almost as a synonym for 'hypothesis'. It is often somewhat misused by students, who might say, perhaps after an unsuccessful experiment, "*Theoretically*, this should have behaved quite differently."

A certain impatience with too much discussion about the philosophical status of laws, hypotheses and theories, has become a characteristic of modern science. This is not necessarily, as non-scientists often assert, additional evidence of the shallowness of the scientifically educated. The point of view has in itself a real importance in science as we have seen in discussing the impact of recent theories upon the mode of thought of physicists.

### The organization of scientific research

In earlier days, research was carried on mostly by wealthy amateurs, or by university professors or college fellows whose main duties lay in teaching. The inspiration of these men was the wish of the scholar to understand and find out as much as possible about the world. It has now become a part of the tradition of university life – especially in science faculties – that the teachers should be expected to pursue research in their subject in order to keep their own knowledge and interest lively and to stimulate, by example, those whom they teach. Even today, when the pace and volume of scientific research is so vastly increased, most of the fundamentally important discoveries still come from the universities.

The profound impact of the discoveries of science upon industry, and more recently upon warfare, has forced industrial organizations and governments to enter the field of science, and they are now by far the largest employers of scientists. However, they devote themselves mainly to the more specific applications of fundamental advances which interest them. One can very roughly classify the two kinds of contribution as pure or applied science, and it is of course with pure science that we have been mainly concerned in this book.

Inevitably, the atmosphere of research laboratories has changed a good deal since Thomson's time. The recent very rapid expansion of science has greatly lowered the average age of scientists (this is especially obvious if one visits a Government establishment such as that devoted to atomic energy at Harwell).

In some branches of science, particularly in the U.S.A., there has recently been the appearance of large 'team' projects which at first sight seem to differ in kind from the 'one-man' project such as the Thomson experiment. It is important to understand how they differ, and yet how much they remain the same. The reason for putting a team of scientists to work on a problem is always the same – complexity. In many of the complex problems in modern biology, for example, it is difficult to make any progress without calling in the services of physicists and chemists, and there now exist in several institutions teams consisting of scientists who might identify themselves separately under any of the following labels: biologist, biophysicist, biochemist, chemist, physicist. At the same time they might be assisted by technicians who were expert, separately, in photography, electronics, X-ray and many other techniques.

In nuclear research, pieces of apparatus have been constructed which cost millions of pounds, designed and run by large teams containing engineers, mathematicians and physicists. Such machines are under the control of pure scientists (although of course Government financial assistance has been called upon) and are not intended to produce atomic bombs or atomic fuel.

The experiments carried out are, in principle, hardly different from the small-scale laboratory experiments carried out by Thomson, or by thousands of research workers all over the world. They are, indeed, logical developments of J. J. Thomson's experiment, and in the same tradition.

# Bibliography

ALLER, L. H. and GOLDBERG, L. *Atoms, Stars and Nebulae.* Churchill (London, 1946).

BLEULER, E. and GOLDSMITH, G. J. *Experimental Nucleonics.* Rinehart (New York, 1952).

BOK, B. J. and P. F. *The Milky Way.* 2nd ed. Churchill (London, 1946).

BORN, M. *Einstein's Theory of Relativity.* Methuen (London, 1924).

BRIDGMAN, P. W. *Reflections of a Physicist.* Philosophical Library (New York, 1950).

CHADWICK, J. *Radioactivity and Radioactive Substances.* Pitman (London, 1953).

CHASE, C. T. *The Evolution of Modern Physics.* Van Nostrand (New York, 1947).

COWLING, T. G. *Molecules in Motion.* Hutchinson (London, 1950).

DAVIDSON, W. L. and POLLARD, E. C. *Applied Nuclear Physics.* Wiley (New York, 1952).

DINGLE, H. *The Scientific Adventure.* Pitman (London, 1952).

EINSTEIN, A. and INFELD, L. *The Evolution of Physics.* Cambridge University Press (Cambridge, 1938).

ELLISON, M.A. *The Sun and its Influence: an introduction to the study of Solar-Terrestrial Relations.* Routledge and Kegan Paul (London, 1955).

GAMOW, G. *The Birth and Death of the Sun.* Macmillan (New York, 1946).

GAMOW, G. *The Creation of the Universe.* Macmillan (New York, 1952).

GLASSTONE, S. *Source Book of Atomic Energy.* Macmillan (London, 1950).

HALLIDAY, D. *Introductory Nuclear Physics.* Wiley (New York, 1950).

HECHT, S. and RABINOWITCH, E. *Explaining the Atom.* Gollancz (London, 1955).

HEITLER, W. *Elementary Wave Mechanics.* Clarendon Press (Oxford, 1950).

HOGBEN, L. *Science for the Citizen.* Allen (London, 1951).

HOUWINK, R. *Elasticity, Plasticity and Structure of Matter.* Cambridge University Press (Cambridge, 1954).

HOYLE, F. *Frontiers of Astronomy.* Heinemann (London, 1955).

HOYLE, F. *The Nature of the Universe.* Blackwell (Oxford, 1950).

HUBBLE, E. P. *The Realm of the Nebulae.* Clarendon Press (Oxford, 1936).

HUBBLE, E. P. *The Observational Approach to Cosmology.* Clarendon Press (Oxford, 1937).

HUME-ROTHERY, W. *Atomic Theory for Students of Metallurgy.* Institute of Metals (London, 1947).

JANOSSY, L. *Cosmic Rays and Nuclear Physics*. Pilot Press (London, 1948).

LAPP, R. E. and ANDREWS, H. L. *Nuclear Radiation Physics*. Pitman (London, 1955).

LENIHAN, J. M. A. *Atomic Energy and its Applications*. Pitman (London, 1954).

LINDSAY, R. B. and MARGENAU, H. *Foundations of Physics*. Chapman and Hall (London, 1949).

LIVINGSTONE, S. *High-energy Accelerators*. Interscience Publishers (New York, 1954).

LONSDALE, K. *Crystals and X-rays*. Bell (London, 1948).

McCREA, W. H. *Physics of the Sun and Stars*. Hutchinson (London, 1950).

MENZEL, D. H. *Our Sun*. Churchill (London, 1949).

MOORE, P. *Guide to the Moon*. Eyre & Spottiswoode (London, 1953).

MOORE, P. *Guide to the Planets*. Eyre & Spottiswoode (London, 1955).

OCCHIALINI, G. P. S. and POWELL, C. F. *Nuclear Physics in Photographs*. Clarendon Press (Oxford, 1947).

PAYNE-GAPOSCHKIN, C. *Stars in the Making*. Eyre & Spottiswoode (London, 1953).

PEIERLS, R. *The Laws of Nature*. Allen and Unwin (London, 1955).

*Physics in Industry. The Acceleration of Particles to High Energies*. Institute of Physics (London, 1950).

PLEDGE, H. T. *Science Since 1500*. Philosophical Library (New York, 1946).

ROTBLAT, J. (Ed.). *Atomic Energy: A Survey*. Taylor and Francis (London, 1954).

SHAPLEY, H. *Galaxies*. Churchill (London, 1947).

SIMON, F. E. et alia. *Low Temperature Physics*. Pergamon Press (London, 1952).

SMART, W. M. *Some Famous Stars*. Longmans, Green (London, 1950).

SPENCER JONES, H. *General Astronomy*. Edward Arnold. 3rd edition (London, 1951).

STRANATHAN, J. D. *The Particles of Modern Physics*. Blakiston (Philadelphia, 1943).

TOULMIN, S. *The Philosophy of Science*. Hutchinson (London, 1953).

DE VAUCOULEURS, G. *The Planet Mars*. Faber (London, 1950).

WATKEYS, C. W. (Ed.). *An Orientation in Science*. McGraw Hill (New York, 1938).

WELLS, A. F. *Structural Inorganic Chemistry*. Clarendon Press (Oxford, 1950).

WHITROW, G. J. *The Structure of the Universe*. Hutchinson (London, 1949).

WILSON, W. *A Hundred Years of Physics*. Duckworth (London. 1950).

# Index